GHRBCK

Nothing but the
TRUTH

LEAH FRIEDMAN

Nothing but the
TRUTH

—— a novel ——

FELDHEIM PUBLISHERS
JERUSALEM · NEW YORK

Translated by Devorah Bindman from the Hebrew *Meyda Gorali* (Jerusalem: Feldheim Publishers, 2001)

First published 2004

ISBN 1-58330-578-5

FELDHEIM PUBLISHERS
POB 43163 / Jerusalem, Israel

208 Airport Executive Park
Nanuet, NY 10954

www.feldheim.com

10 9 8 7 6 5 4 3 2 1

Printed in Israel

Acknowledgments

I would like to express my deep and sincere gratitude to the following:

Mrs. Sue Shmeltzer and her husband, Attorney Tom Shmeltzer, for giving me their precious time answering my many questions and for their constant willingness to provide me with any information I needed for this book.

Attorney Miriam Heilbrun, for her important advice on law and literature.

H. Glazer, for her useful advice and support and for her proofreading of the Hebrew edition of this book.

R. Printz, for her efficient and dedicated work.

Mrs. Kravitz, for all her constructive criticism and suggestions.

Mr. Shai Horowitz, chairman of "Manof," for his kind permission to use and to quote from some of the material that he published.

R' Yaakov Feldheim and all the members of the editorial, design, and production staff of Feldheim Publishers in Jerusalem for their professional work.

R' Yosi Leibler, for his careful work and valuable contribution to this edition.

Rav Mordechai Neugarschal, from whose words this book was born and with whose help and direction it grew and flourished. Special thanks to his wife Leah, whose encouragement, patience, support, and constructive criticism accompanied this book from its inception.

Words cannot adequately express my deep gratitude to you all, each one for his own unique contribution, for without you this book would never have come to be.

Leah Friedman
Jerusalem
Shevat 5764
January 2004

Nothing but the
TRUTH

 THE NIGHT MIST WAS LIFTING. THE GREEN waters of the River Seine burbled gently, and the gray roofs of Paris glistened in the first rays of the sun. In the chill dawn air, the sound of bells was heard from the cathedral towers which rose in their aged somberness.

We stood silently taking in the final scenes of our exciting trip to Europe. The plush tour bus stopped next to us, absorbing into its depths the backpacks that held our few possessions, reminding us of how little man needs to set out to see the world.

The European cities and countryside impressed us, a group of American teenagers, introducing us to a world so different from all the wealth and pampering that we had left behind in our suburban homes.

On our way to the airport we passed the Place de l'Etoile, and sent a last glance towards the monumental arch built by Napoleon III. Through the fog which was quickly dispersing under the sun's rays, we could see the Eiffel Tower, and we thought about all our guide had told us — the scorn of Parisians long ago as they watched its construction. They were derisive of what they considered an ugly metal tower, and even more so of its Jewish designer, Gustave Eiffel, who had undertaken the project for a pioneering international exhibition. Eiffel fought audaciously, confident of the quality and beauty of his work.

With time the Parisians began to understand the tower's technological advantages for telegraph reception and later for radio broadcasting. As the years passed, so too were the special qualities and architectural beauty of the tower acknowledged, so much so that its surroundings were adorned with parks and fountains, and it was adorned with a blaze of lights, becoming the very symbol of Paris. Farewell to you, tower, and *Adieu*, Mr. Eiffel! I thought to myself. You never reaped the fruits of your labor; your countrymen who scorned you reap all the praise...for themselves.

We passed by the palaces, some great and some small, and on our left appeared the impressive opera building, designed by Garnier in the neo-Baroque style. We had become acquainted with its magnificent interior on one of our tours. How different the square looked when empty! And then we passed another square, the Place de la Concorde, looking deserted in its early-morning emptiness. In its center stood the Obelisk of Rameses II, brought from Luxor, Egypt, by Napoleon III to glorify his beloved city.

Here also were the famous Tuileries Gardens, washed and refreshed by the morning dew which made their greenery glisten like jewels. We passed rapidly by the Louvre and its archives, soon reaching the site of the ancient prison fortress, the Bastille. Built by Charles V, we had learned that it was meant as a protection against the rioting citizens, but eventually became the symbol of the French Revolution when the crowds broke through its walls and tore apart its dark cellars.

Farewell to you, liberty, bought with rivers of blood, I whispered. Liberty is sweet, but it leaves a bitter aftertaste.

The bus pounded along the Faubourg road on the way to Charles de Gaulle airport. Now, with the Temple youth group's trip behind me, I could finally relax. I had taken upon myself all the planning and organizing; it had been worthwhile, but the responsibility had weighed heavily on me.

For me, though, only the first part had ended, because unlike the others, I was not going straight back home. I was continuing on to Israel, eager to fulfill my dream. As we approached the airport, my thoughts returned to the day that Rabbi Shneider, the rabbi of our synagogue, had surprised me with the gift of a ticket to Israel.

It was a sunny June morning as I walked towards his home in the exclusive suburb of Lakeside, known for its spacious homes and beautiful parks. Ninety percent of Lakeside's residents were Jewish, and ninety-five percent of them were members of our Reform congregation, one of the largest in the United States.

Jewish settlement in our city had begun in the 1800's, with large groups of immigrants who arrived from central Europe. The Reform movement grew rapidly and developed into a dominant influence on the Jewish schools and organizations.

Rabbi Shneider was proud of the Sunday school classes he had set up. The day school was also under his aegis, among others, and his talents enriched all our educational activities. Our Temple teemed with a variety of cultural and social activities, and on Sabbaths and holidays it bustled with worshipers. Rabbi Shneider's youth groups and his well-funded social activities included many enjoyable and exciting activities.

Two years earlier Rabbi Shneider had appointed me chairperson of the youth group, and now, walking towards his magnificent home, I was planning to discuss with him with my ideas for my group's summer vacation.

"Hi, Amy," Rabbi Shneider greeted me cordially as he waved me through the oak-paneled vestibule, through the luxurious living room and into his office. "I asked you to come today first and foremost so that I could personally express my appreciation of your dedicated work as chairperson of the youth group."

I thanked him for his compliment.

"I was thinking," he went on, "that you deserve a more concrete gesture than just a routine expression of thanks, and so
the Education Committee has decided to present this modest
gift to you."

He handed me a sealed envelope, smiling. I opened it curiously and was surprised to see an airline ticket to Israel, and a
voucher for a stay at Kibbutz Ma'alei Kinneret for four weeks.

"Oh, Rabbi Shneider!" I burst out. "Thank you so much!
Who knows better than you that this has been my longtime
dream! This gift is more than 'modest'!" I was very moved.
"But," I added, "really, how is it that you've changed your
mind?"

Rabbi Shneider smiled. "I chose Israel because I know it has
always been your dream to visit, but I understand what you are
asking. Why did I give you this ticket, even though I rejected
your proposal for a youth group trip?"

I silently nodded my head.

"I'll explain," he said, "but first tell me honestly: My answer
last year didn't sit well with you, did it?"

I blushed in embarrassment. "Didn't sit well" was an under-
statement! Rabbi Shneider had been opposed to our youth
group visiting Israel last summer. He was even opposed to the
national Temple youth group tours every summer. I remembered our conversation well.

> "You want me to give my agreement to a trip to Israel for our teen-
> agers? I'm sorry to disappoint you, but I can't agree to something
> which I oppose in principle!"
>
> "Oppose in principle? What on earth do you mean, Rabbi
> Shneider?"
>
> "Israel is a land of many faces, Amy. It has an enchantment that
> attracts young people, because in its air they breathe an atmo-
> sphere of battles, danger, misguided glory...and also religious ex-
> tremism in various forms. Young people are especially susceptible
> to these things and they turn a blind eye to reason. I have a respon-

sibility towards you, Amy, to the young people of our congregation, and to the parents. I'm also anxious about hastily made decisions to settle there! I can't give my agreement to this. Sorry."

"But you always take the lead in Jewish Agency appeals for Israel, Rabbi Shneider. Many times you've spoken to us about our moral and ethical obligation to support our brothers who live there. Why would it bother you if some of our young people decided to settle there themselves?"

"Look, Amy, I can give speeches and organize appeals for our fellow Jews somewhere, yet under no circumstances would I want to live there myself, even for a day! Surely you understand that."

"No — I don't, Rabbi Shneider!"

"Think of it this way — I could contribute a considerable portion of my wealth to a hospital, but I would not wish to spend even a single day there! We're American Jews, not Israelis."

"I know that it didn't sit well with you." Rabbi Shneider's voice jolted me back to the present conversation, to the plane ticket which he had given me. I remembered how upset I'd been. I'd felt there was something wrong in his analogy, but I didn't know what it was. "You didn't like my personal opinion on the matter," he continued. "But I don't know if you realized that some of my opinions are also the official positions of the Reform Movement."

"What do you mean?" I was startled.

"I see that we must remember to teach the history of our movement to our young people. We have always stood for the complete integration of Judaism with the world around us. Our first generation wanted to fight against anti-Semitism as well as Jewish ignorance and isolationism. For this reason we didn't encourage the 'return to Zion.' In our opinion the 'exile' from the Land of Israel is neither coercion nor punishment, but rather a golden opportunity to enrich the nations with our assets while allowing us to benefit from their culture."

As I listened to Rabbi Shneider, I gazed around the room, at the crystal chandelier, the huge oil paintings in their heavy, engraved frames, the splendor of the classical furniture. It was interesting, I mused, that Rabbi Shneider, who had such modern ideas, would have such conservative, old-fashioned taste.

He pulled out an old bound Reform prayer book from one of the shelves, and opened its yellowed pages. He showed me that many of the prayers with mention of "Zion" or "Jerusalem," had been omitted from that edition.

"This is a Reform prayer book of two generations ago," Rabbi Shneider explained.

I was very upset, but I couldn't express myself. "Then...then has our movement estranged itself from our homeland?"

"I would describe it as taking a clear direction towards achieving ideals in existing conditions," he replied, "instead of aspiring to realize an unrealistic vision. Certainly Reform Judaism relates differently now to Israel. It would be absurd if we, as American Jews, were to ignore the existence of the State of Israel, even though we regard America as our homeland. But we have no interest in encouraging our young people to settle there."

With trepidation I asked, "Did our movement not support the establishment of the State of Israel?"

Rabbi Shneider looked at me. "Oh, let's not worry about such details, Amy," he said. "Let history belong to the past, and we'll deal with the present and the future!"

There was silence in the room.

"Maybe I can tell you something that will make you feel better," he said with a smile. "Our movement had one Rabbi who thought differently — Abba Hillel Silver, of Cleveland, Ohio. He was a really fervent Zionist, and thanks to his tireless activities the Senate adopted a resolution whose operative meaning was support for the future Jewish state. And in 1947, Silver gave a speech at the United Nations together with Ben Gurion, emphasizing that the establishment of the Jewish State should be declared immediately upon the end of the British Mandate."

I let out a sigh of relief. "So our history isn't all negative!"

"It certainly isn't. But you should also know that Rabbi Silver resigned from his position as chairman of the American branch of the Jewish Agency, following an internal dispute with his Reform friends as well as discord with the leadership of the fledgling State of Israel. He didn't make *aliyah* to Israel, nor did he call on the members of his community to do so. And my personal conclusion," said Rabbi Shneider, "is that Reform and Zionism don't exactly go together like peas in a pod.

"That's why my personal stand is that we have an ethical obligation to assist our brethren who live in Israel, and we recognize the historical significance of the country, but we must not nourish any misguided aspirations to settle there. That's what I tried to explain to you last year, apparently without much success.

"Now, I realized that I may not have appreciated how strong your feelings were on the subject. I think that you personally have shown such maturity in your organizational work that I wanted to give you this opportunity. Immediately after the trip to Europe you can go on to Israel while the rest of the group returns home. I've discussed this with your parents, of course. I'm sure that you will have the courage to tell me your impressions afterwards, even if they're negative."

"I'll be happy to share my impressions with you, Rabbi Shneider," I said, "but I have no doubt that they will be very positive."

"We'll wait and see."

Why had he spoken like that? I had no doubt that my impressions would indeed be positive, and I would be very happy to talk to him about them when the time came. Hopefully I could then convince him to allow me to organize a similar trip for my youth group — an exciting and meaningful visit to the Land of Israel.

 KIBBUTZ MA'ALEI KINNERET ROSE ABOVE the Arbel valley, an enchanting and attractive place, a green island gilded in rays of sunshine, situated majestically above the azure of Lake Kinneret. To the right and to the left it was overshadowed by rocky cliffs that plunged downwards in twisting paths towards the lake.

I loved to look out at the view of the valley from my window, especially in the late afternoon or at sunrise. For me these moments were a Heavenly gift, a momentary relief from the loneliness that I was suffering.

What a foolish mistake I had made! To land in a foreign country in the middle of the Middle Eastern summer, without a full command of the language, bombarded by a totally different mentality, bereft of family or friends. And under these circumstances to try and become integrated into an organized daily routine!

As a volunteer, I was welcomed hospitably and given a pleasant room. The kibbutz members showed me the communal orchards, the jewelry factory, the library, the swimming pool, the youth clubhouse, and the dining room. They explained to me in fluent English how volunteers fit into the life of the kibbutz, and told me a little about their history and the ideals of the founders.

But for all their friendliness I felt so strange and different, a stranger in a strange land. The language confused me as well — I had studied Hebrew, but spoken Israeli Hebrew seemed to be completely different from the language I thought I knew. I had hoped that the young people would speak English to me like their parents did, but they found it difficult and just didn't try. I found the company of the adults pleasant, but I was lonely.

After several days I began to feel rejected and unwanted. I thought of the wonderful trip my friends and I had spent together, and I wondered why I had come here. Perhaps Rabbi Shneider had been wrong — there was absolutely no chance that our Temple youth would have wanted to stay here!

I hadn't found any of the things I was searching for. It didn't feel more "Jewish" to me than my neighborhood at home, and I didn't feel more connected to "the Jewish People."

Well, I consoled myself, when my two weeks as a volunteer are over, I'll be part of the young people's group touring the country, going to Jerusalem, seeing everything. Maybe then I'll feel better.

On the first Friday night, I stood admiring the sunset, which painted the entire valley in deep reds and purples. The setting sun majestically ushered in the Shabbos. Night fell immediately — there was no dusk here.

Dressed in my pink Shabbos suit, I left my room and walked along the kibbutz path, holding my Siddur in hand, looking for someone to ask where the synagogue was. I greeted the first person I saw, and asked her.

The woman's response to my "Good Shabbos" and my question was laughter. "Synagogue? Prayers? Are you Orthodox?"

"No," I answered, bewildered, "I'm Reform."

She shrugged her shoulders and said, "Sorry, here we don't have Shabbos and we don't have prayers!" She turned to go on her way.

I returned to the solitude of my room and tried to make sense out of what had happened. No prayers on Shabbos? How could that be? I asked myself. Other than the language and the fact that the place was marked on the map as Israel, what set this place apart as Jewish? At least where I came from Shabbos meant prayers, a festive meal and a feeling of family warmth, but here on the kibbutz the meal was the usual supper, with no Jewish element to be seen.

I sat wearing my festive clothing while my heart mourned. No, this was not what I had expected! It had been obvious to me that in Israel the Jews would be somehow much more "Jewish" than the Jews I knew.

*   *   *

One very hot evening, I was assigned a shift in the communal dining hall. The air outside was humid and suffocating. I was still immersed in my loneliness, even though I had become acquainted with several young people on the kibbutz, and had even gone with them on a beautiful trip to Ein Gev, on the eastern shore of the Kinneret.

As I walked into the huge stainless-steel kitchen, an elderly woman with a pleasant face looked up from the vegetables she had been rinsing. "Hello," she said, smiling. "What's your name?" The fact that she addressed me in my own language endeared her to me immediately.

"Amy," I replied.

"Nice to meet you, Amy. My name is Chana," she said, "but despite my age everybody calls me 'Chana'le'."

"It's a nice name," I responded, and she laughed.

"I am happy to see you," she continued as if talking to an old acquaintance. "You remind me of all the happy groups of young people that visit our kibbutz during the school vacation."

"Happy groups?" I asked.

"Oh, yes," she said. "They bring joy to all of us, especially to the older people. I see you came by yourself. You're not the first one to do so, but it's always hard when you're not with a group. It can be lonely."

Without knowing it, she had touched a very sensitive nerve. I nodded, and mumbled, "Yes, it is."

Chana'le looked at me with her discerning blue eyes. "You probably feel alone and strange, and find it difficult to get used to your surroundings. I assure you that if you had come with a group, things would look completely different."

Something in her words made me think of Rabbi Shneider — he was the one who had actually created this situation. When I'd wanted to come with a group he'd refused. He had bought me this ticket. Had he known for himself what Chana'le had told me?

"Come, Amy," she said cheerfully, "if you can cut up these vegetables for the salad, I'll make the soup."

I began to cut up the beautiful tomatoes, cucumbers, and green peppers almost mechanically. Chana'le asked me questions about myself: where I lived, what my parents did, my studies. By the time the salad was ready she could have written my biography! Her manner was pleasant and warm; she knew how to listen and when she asked questions they were caring, rather than probing. Her fluent English and the fact that she seemed genuinely interested in me gave me, for the first time since coming to the kibbutz, the feeling that I had finally found a friend — but she was at least seventy years old and I was seventeen.

"I heard that you were looking for a place to pray on Shabbos," she said suddenly.

I raised astonished eyes towards her.

"Don't be so surprised," she said with a smile. "A kibbutz is like a family — everyone knows everyone else. There are no secrets here! You're used to praying?"

I nodded my head.

"And our kitchen doesn't bother you?"

"Kitchen? What do you mean?"

"The food here isn't kosher, you know."

"Oh, I don't eat kosher," I replied.

Now it was Chana'le's turn to be amazed. "How can it be that you're careful about prayer but not about *kashrus*?" she questioned.

"We're Reform," I said, convinced that the power of that assertion would be answer enough for her.

"I come from an assimilated home," she said quietly, "but I know a little about religion. I've never heard of Jews who pray but don't keep kosher!" She was silent, caught in her own thoughts. Then she spoke, "If you'd like to visit me after work, I'll tell you why I'm sensitive about *kashrus*."

That night I spent the first of many hours in Chana's small, well-kept home. As I listened to her fascinating story, I realized I was hearing a witness to the most tragic events of our time.

"I WAS BORN IN HOLLAND," CHANA'LE BEGAN. "I was called Anna then. My family had lived in Holland for generations, but I want to tell you about the darkness that fell upon us there — the period of the German occupation. At the time I was a young wife and mother. My one-year-old son, Daniel, was a very beautiful, plump baby boy, with golden curls and shining green eyes. He had two dimples on his cheeks and when he laughed the heavens laughed with him. Hans, my husband, was a surgeon in Amsterdam's central hospital. I also worked there. I was a nurse.

"Hans had nerves of steel, and when he performed operations his colleagues were always amazed at his control. His hands never trembled; they functioned like deft and skilled machines. He was held in great esteem among his colleagues, despite his young age.

Chana'le sighed. "If Hans hadn't had nerves of steel," she said quietly, "perhaps we would have gone through the war differently. But he was *too* optimistic and calm, at a time when fear could have — should have — moved us to seek refuge.

"The Germans occupied Holland during the summer of 1940. During the weeks that followed, we didn't notice any of the signs that characterized the German occupation in Eastern Europe. On the contrary — life just continued on in its usual pattern. Other than the arrogant manner of the Gestapo officers as they made their presence felt throughout the city, everything seemed the same.

"And when the first decrees came, even though we understood their anti-Semitic intent, they were worded in such a way that you couldn't really say that they were discriminatory. I remember the law to prevent 'cruelty in slaughter,' which prohibited Jewish *shechitah*. A short while after that the Reich Commissioner was given permission to fire civil servants. Thus it became legal to give many Jewish workers letters of dismissal.

"In October, clear anti-Semitic directives appeared. All Jews were required to fill out special forms declaring their Jewishness. A census of all Jewish businesses was taken, so that they could be expropriated methodically in the future.

"During those days, when the threat of the sword hung in the air, I pleaded with Hans to make contact with the Dutch underground. 'My uncle Benjamin has already brought two of his children to Dutch families with the help of the underground. They'll be safe there, whatever happens. He said he could help us, too — please!' I begged him.

"'Anna,' he would say, 'when will you stop being so frightened? Why are you so worried? The Dutch are our friends, and they will never let the Germans harm us.'

"But my heart told me otherwise, and I could not understand where Hans and others like him drew their optimism," Chana'le went on. "In June 1941 we received notification to report to the Amsterdam City Hall to receive new identity cards — stamped with the letter 'J'. Most of the Jews who registered there, about 80,000, were later transported to the East, to the death camps. But we, in our naiveté, stood quietly and politely, took the new identity cards, and returned home to live our quiet lives without feeling the earth quaking beneath our feet.

"One night my cousin Max arrived at our house. He was as pale as death and talked to us for a long time. He had heard from reliable sources about the fate of 400 young Jews whom the Germans had snatched in the streets. They had been taken to Buchenwald and then to Mauthausen, where they worked at tortuous, hard labor. They were forced to hew huge stones in a pit, and then had to bring them up the mountain with their bare hands. But the story didn't end there. Recently most of the families of these young people had received death certificates from the German authorities!

"Max was silent. Five of his friends had been there. 'They murdered them... they murdered them,' he kept repeating. 'It can't be that suddenly they all died, young and strong.'

"When Max left our house I grabbed Hans's hand, hysterical with fear. 'We must run away immediately and hide! Can't you see what's happening!'

"But Hans silenced me. 'Anna, calm down. Nothing will come out of hysteria. If Max's story is true, the Dutch authorities will deal seriously with it. You'll see.'

"The Jewish council did in fact verify the matter and dispatched letters of protest, but what did that help? The Germans had learned a lesson: They continued to murder, but didn't send any more death certificates.

"One night, towards the end of September 1942, we were awakened by the sound of screams. I froze in fear. Hans jumped up and rushed to the window. Trembling, I got up and stood by his side. Through the slats in the shutter, we saw a black limousine with the ominous SS symbol parked in the street. We watched in silent horror as German soldiers kicked at the door of a house and shouted until it was opened. They dragged the people out of their house and into the car, kicking them and beating them. As the car disappeared around the corner, terrified neighbors came out and looked at each other helplessly.

"'Hans, Hans,' I wept, 'What's going to be? What if they come and take *us* tomorrow? And what will happen to Daniel?'

"Hans remained silent. It was the first time that he didn't try to quiet me or to calm my fears.

"'I will not leave him with Julia anymore,' I said.

"'So what will you do?' he asked me.

"'I'll take him to work with us and leave him in your room. We'll arrange our times so that at every break one of us will be with him.'

"'All right,' Hans sighed. 'I'll have to tell Professor Heinrich about it.'

"'No, don't tell him! You have a private room, what difference does it make to him who's there? It can be our son's hiding place, and if the Professor hears about it then for sure others will too.'

"'And how will you bring him into the hospital with no one noticing?'

"'Inside my fur coat.'

"'And if he cries?'

"'Your room is at the end of the hall — not many people pass by there. If there's any problem we...we can use a sedative,' I concluded quietly.

"Hans was shocked. 'You'd go that far?'

"I nodded my head mutely. 'If you could make a connection with the underground, we could flee. It could save us, Hans, and our son.'

"Hans promised me that he would do what he could. We continued to ride our bicycles to and from work every day with our treasure hidden in a basket, wrapped in a fur coat. We left the house very early, hidden by the morning darkness, pedaling breathlessly until the hospital gates closed behind us.

"The days were charged with tension and anxiety. Every day, new edicts and evictions were published in the *Joodische Veekblad*, the official mouthpiece of the Jewish community. The noose tightened around us. Hans contacted a member of the underground, who took our personal details and photographs in order to prepare false identity cards for us. He promised to keep in touch with us.

"In the spring of 1942 the big expulsions began in Holland. Hoss Der Funten was appointed to fill the expulsion quotas. One of the ways he filled them was by snatching weak Jews from mental hospitals.

"Hans again contacted the member of the underground who promised to find a family to shelter us in a village. 'If you agree to separate, it will be easier for us to find you a foster family,' he said. We found the thought unbearable, but then the great raid on the Jewish hospital, Nederlands Israelitisch Hospitalie, took place. The Germans dragged ailing patients out of their beds and into trucks — and also took Jewish members of the staff in order to fill their quota.

"The underground made contact with us. It seemed that within a week they would transfer us to a village in the south of Holland. Daniel had gotten used to staying in Hans's room alone with a few toys. He would sit quietly and play or nap. We didn't have to give him any sedatives, thank God. A smile would light up his serious face when he heard the door open and he would see me or Hans coming to visit him. Apparently he also felt the anxiety and tension and adapted himself to it. In the evenings we left the hospital early, because we were afraid of the nightly curfew and the SS soldiers who patrolled the streets. My fur coat continued to serve as a hiding place for our tiny son. We counted the days until the redeeming announcement would come that a foster family had been found for us.

"It was a rainy morning at the end of March when awful screams were heard in the hospital's corridors. SS officers broke into the rooms and ordered the patients to get up and stand in straight lines against the wall. They collected their identity cards, studied them, and began to read out Jewish names; every patient whose name was called was commanded to go out to the trucks. Patients who couldn't walk were supported by their friends. It was a nightmare march. The Nazis screamed curses and pushed them forward. Hans and I stared at each other unbelievingly. They had reached our refuge.

"Hans held my hand tightly and whispered: 'Trust me, Anna. We won't go with them.' I trusted him — but he was wrong. After the Jewish patients had been removed, the SS officer read the staff list. He turned to Professor Heinrich, the director of the hospital, and asked for a private meeting in his office.

"After a few minutes they emerged. Professor Heinrich's face was as gray as sackcloth. He indicated with a gesture that he had no choice. We, the staff members, were stood against the wall where the patients had been. Our identity cards were taken from us, and the Jewish names were again called out. We were commanded to go out to the trucks. My heart beat violently. Daniel! Hans whispered to me, 'Maybe we should leave him here, maybe he will be saved!'

"'No, absolutely not! I will not abandon my son.' Hans didn't stop me. He signaled to Professor Heinrich that I was going to the washroom. The Professor told the SS officer who looked at me for a moment and then screamed in German: 'Fast! Fast!' I flew like an arrow from its bow. With a trembling hand I wrapped my son in the fur coat and returned to the row, which already had fewer people. The German suddenly called Hans's name. Professor Heinrich tried to whisper something in his ear, but the German rudely shoved him backwards.

"The staff members looked at Hans. Standing straighter than usual he strode towards the steps and stood there waiting. For me, for us. I heard my name being called. Professor Heinrich didn't even try to intervene. Trembling with my precious burden, I went to my husband's side. Many eyes looked at us in sorrow. We had been an important part of the hospital's staff, but terror prevented our friends from extending a hand at this difficult hour.

"The trucks roared powerfully, crying out against us, the Jews, who were being taken from the land of the living to the land of death.

"So began the horrific journey to Auschwitz. From the trucks we were crowded like sardines into train cars, under a hail of curses and screams. And still my Hans whispered to me, 'Trust me, my dear, we will still get through this.' Hans's nerves of steel were still working."

Chana'le fell silent. "Hans supported me continuously during that terrible journey, keeping me from despair. But," she sighed, "it was not in his power to save our lives.

"He had been an amazing surgeon — but he wasn't God."

Chana'le shook herself and looked at me with a sorrowful smile. "It happened so long ago, but I still can't help myself from wondering what might have been if Hans had tried to contact the Dutch underground two weeks earlier."

Chana'le paced up and down in the pleasant, comfortable room, unwittingly fingering the lovely flower box in the window. Suddenly she went to the small sideboard and took out a little album. She silently opened it and pointed to the photograph of a young man. He had a sensitive Jewish face. His eyes were intelligent and he looked determined. One crease in his forehead gave him that dignified look that is seen on people who think a lot.

"Hans," she whispered.

She turned the page and I saw that her fingers were trembling. She didn't have to tell me whose picture was there. I knew that the lovely baby dressed in the sailor suit was Daniel.

"Angel, little angel," whispered Chana'le, her eyes brimming with tears. "These are the only photos of them I have. My cousin Max brought them to me after the war." Chana'le turned a page and I saw the picture of a lovely, blooming young woman in her twenties.

"Chana'le — is that you?" This time it was I who whispered.

"I've changed, haven't I," she said, her voice choking. "Suffering has left its mark. But my loved ones haven't changed.

They will remain young and beautiful forever." A cold wind blew in from the window. The hour was late.

I stood up, thinking it would be best if I left, leaving her to extinguish the flames of her memories at her own pace. Chana'le understood my intention and asked, "Am I burdening you with too heavy a load?'

"Oh, no, not at all," I told her. "I just thought that maybe you wanted to rest a bit."

"Rest?" she laughed hollowly. "It won't take long before I'll be resting from it all. But as long as I am here," her voice became strong, "I have to work and produce. To remember and to remind others. Do you understand? I am telling you this story so that you will be able understand our conversation in the kitchen, and why I was so surprised that you don't eat kosher food. Please let me continue."

Chana'le made us a cool drink, and then went on.

"So many people were crushed into the car that it was impossible to move a hand or a foot. But that was just the beginning of a trip that was unlike any other. The thirst in our throats burned like fire. People groaned and suffocated. Daniel stopped whimpering and lay in my arms apathetically.

"Hans tried to find water, 'Maybe someone has some water for a baby?' he called out. Water, the elixir of life in this hell, but there was no water.

"Daniel trembled in my arms. My tears fell on his face and he lifted his pure eyes up to me, as if he understood that it was not within my power to give him what he needed.

"The hours ticked on and the train pushed on stubbornly as the nightmare turned into a living hell. The bodies stuck to one another, and the thirst sapped our remaining strength. Little by little, people began to die. Passengers became corpses and it was almost impossible to breathe. Daniel lay still in my arms. Hans kept his eyes on him and on me. Both of us knew that our baby had only a few hours left.

"Just then the train began to slow down, and the silence of the engine told us that we had reached our destination, wherever that was. The doors opened and a gust of cold, refreshing air hit our faces. In my innocence I thought that wherever we were, and whatever awaited us, it couldn't be worse than what we had just been through. But again I learned through bitter experience that man knows little indeed about hell. Then, before we entered the gates of Auschwitz, we still knew very little about the extent of the evil that mankind is capable of perpetrating.

"They pushed us out of the train car with bestial cries and blows. Our legs, paralyzed from continued standing, would not budge, and we swayed like drunks, stumbling and falling, comprehending nothing. There was only fear, indescribable terror, and blows that burned the flesh as they struck. Somehow we managed to stand in straight rows, the women on one side and the men on the other.

"In vain my eyes searched for Hans, for a parting glance, an unspoken message of hope that we might yet meet again — but nothing. Hans disappeared and I never saw him again.

"I clutched Daniel in my arms. 'Water, water,' my lips whispered. But to my left and to my right there were only rows, rows of women, children, SS officers. The prisoners were grotesque and skeletal, with glazed eyes and shaven heads, dressed in striped clothing that hung on their emaciated bodies. They took charge of the piles of personal possessions that were left behind us.

"As I stared at them, terrified, one of them came up to me. Gripped with horror, I clutched my son to my heart, while the skeleton whispered to me in Yiddish: 'Give your child to the old woman behind you, quickly!'

"'Insane, mad!' I thought to myself. Where can I run away from him, if everything here is insanity enmeshed in bonds of death? I clutched Daniel tighter and the man continued to look at me with his glazed eyes: 'Quickly, fool! Give her your child.'

"And then suddenly he grabbed my son from me and ran! I cried out and turned to run after him, but a sharp blow to my head forced me to the ground. Who picked me up, who pushed me forward in the line, who supported me, how did they choose me — to go to the right? I remember nothing. Fogginess and numbness of all my senses and feelings enveloped me entirely.

"In my first hour at the gates of Auschwitz, I lost my husband, I lost my son, I lost my reason to go on living."

"I FOUND MYSELF IN A LONG WOODEN HUT, together with about ten other women who were shaking from the cold like I was. One of them, Lena, tried to get me to talk, but nothing. I stared at her and at what was going on around me as if in a dream. However, she didn't give up, and she held my hand like a compassionate mother. She talked to me. She talked about hope and said that the war was coming to an end, and that we had to believe in our God Who would bring us out from darkness to light. She said that we had only to trust in Him and to believe strongly and then we would merit to see the liberation with our own eyes.

"For some reason Lena's words reached me. I cried, 'And what will become of my son, my son?' And then I wept, I wept as I had never wept in all my life. She hugged me and tried to calm me. 'What happened to your son?' she asked gently.

"'They grabbed him from my arms.'

"'Who grabbed him?'

"'A crazy man with striped clothing. He told me to give my son to an old woman, and when I refused he grabbed him and ran away. I tried to run after him but they hit me on the head and I collapsed.'

"Lena looked straight into my eyes. I will never forget what she said to me. 'You are crying about that, my dear girl? The man was a Jewish prisoner, and if he grabbed your son from your hands he did so in order to save him! You don't know,' she whispered as if telling me a great secret, 'that in this place there are no children — not even one. He certainly must have smuggled your son to one of the non-Jewish workers near the train, so that they would keep him alive. And you are crying? You should be happy and grateful.'

"'What? What are you saying?' I grasped at the fine thread of hope. Again Lena repeated what she had said, and comforted me. She told me that some of the prisoners did that. 'They see the deliveries, and know what will happen, and therefore they take advantage of the first confusion to save the children.'

"'But how will I find my son?'

"'Don't worry, when the war ends you and the other mothers will tell the people in charge the date you arrived in Auschwitz, and the Jews who saved these children will tell you whom they gave the children to. That way you will find them alive and well.'

"Lena breathed new life into me. I know with complete certainty that if it hadn't been for her words, I would have put an end to my life by running towards the electrified fence.

"Every day she nurtured within me the hope that one day I would be reunited with my son and my husband. 'He's young, your husband,' she told me authoritatively. 'They need him for work, and you will meet him in the end — and the end is near. Some of the Jews in the camp who work outside have received information that Germany has suffered one defeat after another. Be strong, my dear, and soon it will all be over.'

"The days passed slowly. I worked in the sewing workshop. In my youth my mother had encouraged me to learn to sew, and that skill was now my salvation. Lena had recommended me to the overseer as an excellent seamstress, so he had assigned me to their work group. We repaired the uniforms of the SS officers and we sewed them coats. I didn't realize then how lucky I was to have been placed with that group. I wasn't yet familiar with the hard labor of Auschwitz. For me this work was hard enough, especially because of the terrible hunger that was always present.

"Lena's words were my sustenance during those dark days."

*   *   *

"Lena was Orthodox and her faith blazed within her. Never did I hear from her a word of worry, of despair, or a sigh for her own suffering. It could be that because of that I assumed she was childless. Until the day of her death I didn't know that she had lost her six children in the Lodz ghetto.

"I don't know how, but she always knew what holiday it was and made sure to let us know. I remember how she conducted a Seder on Pesach with another few girls and women. They sat on the bunk and recited the words of the Haggadah, even though they had nothing apart from the 'bitter herbs' of Auschwitz. Even so they sang the special Pesach songs with feeling. There was one woman there who sang so well that our eyes filled with tears. We watched them with great admiration. Where did they get the strength of spirit to celebrate the holiday of freedom deep in the mire of slavery?

"Lena was a treasure for all of us. She showered all of us with warmth and hope; she was like a mother and a sister.

"Because we loved and admired her so much, we were very frightened when new "selections" were made. She was older than we were and that was enough to put her in danger. Three times she passed, but on the fourth time she did not. Mengele, may his name be erased, stood there, the embodiment of the devil himself, and with his rod pointed to the left. We stared at her, refusing to believe, but she smiled at us and cried out, 'Be strong, girls. God will be with you and protect you.'

"I just could not tear my eyes away from Lena's beautiful, heroic, and fragile face.

"She looked at me for a moment and said words to me that I

didn't understand: 'Anna, forgive me — everything that I did, I did for you.' And then she added, 'Don't be sorry for me, I am going calmly. My six beloved children are waiting for me to return. I did everything I could to survive, but the Holy One, Blessed be He, wanted something else. But you — continue to live, continue to encourage the others.'

"She ignored all the screams of the women around her and went calmly. I saw her supporting two women who were next to her as they boarded the trucks.

"That was Lena.

"How would I survive without her? I asked myself. And I could see that the other women were thinking the same thing. Our hut was in mourning — something out of the ordinary for Auschwitz, where death was commonplace and life was out of the ordinary.

"Every day the chimneys of Auschwitz belched out human smoke. Every day women's corpses were piled up.

"I wanted to do something to honor the memory of Lena. In Auschwitz there were no graves, no markers to erect. No memorial candles. Suddenly a thought came into my head: perhaps I could honor the memory of this noble woman by taking on some behavior that was important to her. But what? Could I comfort others? I was too closed up in myself and my sorrow.

"Then it came to me: I would keep kosher. You must understand that to keep kosher in Auschwitz meant, very simply, giving up a portion of life on a daily basis. There were minuscule pieces of horsemeat mixed in the thin soup that sustained us, but Lena had been careful not to eat it. The thin, dry slices of sausage that were occasionally given out were also made from horsemeat. I knew that if I abstained from these I would get hungrier and hungrier, because abstention had a false psychological effect, as if the thin portion that was missing had the ability to give a feeling of satiety.

"Looking back I think that I chose to do this because for me,

as an assimilated Jew, it seemed like such an impossible com-
mandment to keep in Auschwitz. But Lena had proven to me
that this was in the realm of the possible, if only one truly wanted
it. I adhered to Lena's image, hoping to rise above myself in at
least one respect, as she had done.

"It was difficult for me," said Chana'le. She was silent for
several long moments. "But I stood by my decision. Once,
when my resolve was failing me, I found myself saying, 'Lena,
you did so much for me; let me do this one thing for you!' And I
was able to continue with my last reserves of energy.

"When the Russians reached the gates of Auschwitz I was
one of the few still left alive. Almost a walking corpse, I weighed
thirty kilos — about sixty-five pounds — and my spindly legs
couldn't carry me any longer. I thought to myself that with liberation my struggle on this earth had come to an end, but it was
not to be so.

"When I opened my eyes I found myself in a kind of field
hospital. I don't know what they fed me, because most of the
time reality was blurred, but when I finally got up and began to
walk around the camp, I realized that I would continue my battle
to eat only kosher food. I began to exchange the meat for bread,
and I was always hungry. Then a group was organized which received permission to cook for itself. I joined them, and my days
of hunger were over. It was time to search for my husband and
child.

"I had difficulty getting information about Daniel, but I
heard about Hans very quickly. I met an old friend of ours, who
recognized me. His own face had changed beyond recognition.
I asked him about my husband but he tried to evade me.

"'Please,' I said to him, 'I've had no word about Hans since
we got to Auschwitz. If you have any scrap of information, whatever it is, don't keep it from me.'

"He looked at me straight in the eye. 'He died, several days
after you arrived.' His words were like a blow. But then I wanted

the details. And he knew them. When the Germans had informed Hans that he would be working in his profession in the camp, he was very happy. Apparently he thought he would be able to treat the prisoners, but in fact he was referred to the infamous Block 10. Hans didn't know anything about it, or about the horrific "experiments" that were conducted there.

"Mengele prepared a detailed work program for him that included a series of operations. When Hans returned to the prisoners' hut after completing the first day's work, he refused to tell the others what he had seen, but he did tell them clearly of his intention to commit suicide. A few days later his friends saw his body, and the rumor spread that he had swallowed cyanide in Block 10.

"'Lost and despairing, I continued my search for Daniel. Although I had hoped to find my husband alive, there had always been a fear in the back of my mind that I would never see him again. It was a kind of inner knowledge that had accompanied me from the moment our feet touched the ground of Auschwitz. When I heard our friend's story I knew it was the truth.

"But it was not so with Daniel. I kept on envisioning him with his heart-capturing smile, his eyes that shone with happiness. He was with me everywhere, and it was this anticipation and hope that gave me the desire to keep on living.

"Where was Daniel? I began to question every woman there — perhaps she had heard of prisoners who hid or passed on children to the neighboring villagers? But no one had heard of such a thing.

"One sympathetic woman, Rivka, understood what the problem was and began to question my sources of information. As I told her everything, she looked at me with a peculiar expression on her face. Pity? Horror? Something else? I couldn't tell.

"Finally she sighed deeply. 'Your story is a fantasy. Something like that could never have happened in Auschwitz,' she said quietly. 'Prisoners could not smuggle children near the train! Anyway, most of the local villagers collaborated with the Germans. In my opinion Lena wanted to save *your* life, and that's why she told you what she told you. Otherwise you would have lost your will to live.'

"'No!' I cried. 'That cannot be.'

"'I'm not making this up,' she said. 'They also snatched my little daughter from my arms... and I also screamed and received a terrible blow on my head. Immediately, though, the others explained to me that the man had saved my life, because my daughter's fate was already sealed. I understand your pain — I carry the same pain within me — but you mustn't waste the little strength you have left searching for a child who will never return.'

"We simply looked at each other, two mothers grieving for their lost children. Then she said to me, 'I have nothing more to look for here. My husband did not survive, and neither did my daughter. My whole family perished. I am going to settle in Eretz Yisrael, and perhaps there I will be able to start over again. Will you come with me?'

"I nodded my head silently. Rivka accompanied me all the way, which made my pain and loneliness easier to bear, but when we reached the shores of Eretz Yisrael, she was sent to a different kibbutz. Again I found myself alone, at the entrance to an unknown country."

Chana'le was silent. She took a sip from her cup and then said, as if to herself, "Lena saved my life. She understood that without hope, I would have thrown myself onto the fence. That's what she meant by her last words: *Anna, forgive me — everything that I did, I did for you.* It took me time to understand that.

"But by the time I walked into the kibbutz, I had come to accept what Lena did for me. I knew that it was because of her that I was here, and that I was capable of beginning a new life in this land that was being renewed, this Land of my Fathers. Because of that, I decided that I would continue to keep kosher in her memory.

"I was certain that here I would not be forced to fight about *kashrus*. Surely on a Jewish kibbutz in the Land of Israel everyone would eat kosher food, only kosher food!"

Chana'le raised her eyes to me and smiled ironically. "You were very disappointed that a kibbutz in Israel didn't have Shabbos services? Then you can imagine how shocked *I* was when I discovered that my kibbutz didn't serve kosher food! It seemed obvious to me that in a land where everyone was Jewish, the basic tenets of Judaism would be kept... until the day I was on duty in the kitchen."

She laughed bitterly as she described to me her shock when she saw meat and milk together, and when she realized that the chickens were killed by a blow instead of by kosher slaughter. "I fled from the kitchen and ran straight to the kibbutz secretary. I asked him how it was possible that here they didn't keep kosher! He sat quietly as I described everything that I had seen in the kitchen, and when I was finished, he spoke. 'Anna,' he said gently, 'you are a member of our kibbutz. We can share with you what we have, but we cannot give you what we don't have: Here there is not and never will be kosher food!'

"I didn't eat anything that day, nor the following. On the second night of my fast I lay on my bed staring at the ceiling and wishing I could die. 'What will happen to me?' I whispered. 'Who will give me food? Can it be that after all I've been through I will die from hunger in Eretz Yisrael?'

"My forced encounter with that familiar hunger, together with the fact that no one seemed to have noticed my absence, deepened my pain. I had no strength and I was in terrible distress.

"At that point I had a visitor. Aryeh, one of the prominent figures on the kibbutz, came into my room. He stopped at the sight of me, and just stood there staring, unable to utter a word.

'Chana'le!' he finally cried. 'What's wrong? Are you sick?'

"I shook my head.

"'How many days have you been lying here like this?'

"I lifted two fingers.

"How is it possible that here on the kibbutz no one knows where you are?' he asked me in his booming voice, as if I could possibly answer him. 'Have you had anything to eat? To drink?'

"I shook my head again. He ranted and raved against the entire kibbutz, and stormed out.

"Within a few minutes the kibbutz nurse and several other people were standing around me. They were all speaking, but I couldn't understand what they were saying. The nurse connected me to an infusion, and gave me an injection. Every time I opened my eyes I saw Aryeh's concerned face, watching me with a father's worry for his daughter. It was his concern and care that saved me." Chana'le was silent. "Shortly afterwards I married him."

Again she was silent. "When I got up from my sickbed I knew that I would stay on the kibbutz, and that I would try to establish a new home. I also knew that I would have to eat.

"Pangs of conscience are a difficult thing to erase," she said. "My conscience will follow me to the grave. After Lena died, I promised myself that I would honor her memory. I promised, and I kept my promise in Auschwitz — but here in the Land of Israel I didn't!

"About ten years ago a group of kibbutz members decided to become vegetarians — I added my name to the list, and became a vegetarian too! We have vegetarian meals available in the communal dining hall, and so in this way I can also keep kosher again. At least I'm not eating milk and meat together, or animals that haven't been slaughtered correctly," she said with a sorrowful smile.

"So, Amy — now do you understand why I was surprised when I discovered that you, with a religious background, pray but don't keep kosher?"

I was ashamed. It was the first time in my life that I felt some kind of fault in the Reform Judaism that I had grown up with. I had always harbored the desire for more, a little more Judaism, a little more tradition, but even so I had never felt that our way was distorted or faulty. Suddenly a window had opened, but I didn't quite understand what I had seen.

MY FEELINGS OF ALIENATION ON THE KIBBUTZ disappeared when I began to take part in Effy Yavin's guided tours of Israel. Effy was short in height, but great in everything he did. With his thick, curly mustache and an Israeli *kova tembel* perched on his head, his very appearance could bring a smile. When he opened his mouth, though, we all realized how serious this man was.

Effy gave us, a group of *chevre* — the young people from the kibbutz — guided tours of the country for two weeks, with a few small breaks, and my days became full of meaning and content. He was an expert in all the historical treasures of Jewish history in Eretz Yisrael throughout all the generations. He knew every stone and every plant, and for every pathway he had a historical tale.

Traveling together, I began to feel a part of the group. Effy spoke fluent English, and was happy to repeat and explain to me everything that I hadn't understood in his rapid Hebrew.

We "did" the country, from Eilat till Mount Hermon, navigating many of the routes by ourselves using maps and compasses. Several times we crossed natural obstacles by swimming or rappelling, and there were long hikes where we walked for hours in the hot Mediterranean sun.

Out of all the regions of the country, I loved the Golan

Heights the most; the open spaces, natural springs, the view of Lake Kinneret. Gamla with its heroic history from ancient times, Tel Pars and the Chushnia Valley, the battle stories from the Yom Kippur War, were all brought to life by Effy.

He enriched my meager knowledge of the history of my people and of Eretz Yisrael, and answered all my questions with patience.

Towards the end of the first week we set out on a trip to Zavitan Meshoshim. It was a particularly hot day, and Effy made sure that we drank every ten minutes. We marched on foot for what felt like many miles through the parched, yellow countryside until we were rewarded with our view of the Zavitan cliffs rising up from behind the thicket of dense green vegetation. It was so exhilarating to come to the sparkling waterfall on this hot day that we all jumped into the pool at its base wearing our clothes! Effy sat in a shaded corner, looking over his maps and books as usual. Slowly we all came out of the cold water to dry off while sitting on the boulders.

And then the drama began.

Danny started to climb up the cliff, boulder by boulder; using his hands and his feet, maneuvering and climbing until he reached a height of forty feet. At that point he called out cheerfully, "One, two and... three!" and then he jumped. I stared with horror at the sight; there were huge rocks in the pool, and I wondered how he would have jumped so fearlessly from such a height.

The *chevre* cheered loudly as Danny's head emerged from the water. After him Yoav climbed up and jumped, then Gabi and Lior, each one trying to climb one boulder higher than his friend. Of all the boys, only Eitan still sat on the side, not even trying to rise to the challenge.

"Come on, come on, Eitan," yelled his brave companions from the pool. "Are you a commando, or aren't you?" they taunted. (Of course I didn't understand what they meant until the military context was explained.)

Eitan didn't reply.

"Coward, coward!" they began to chant. "Who'd accept you for a commando unit? What do you think, only marks count? Courage is what counts! Come on, let's see you jump! Army rating 21!" each one echoed after the other.

I saw Eitan's face getter paler and paler, with the *chevre* teasing him fervently. Suddenly he got up, his lips closed tightly like someone who has reached a fateful decision. He climbed quickly up the boulders, clearly trying to overcome his fear and rid himself of the nightmare.

"Yay, Eitan! Yay, Eitan!" Now there were calls of encouragement. He climbed on, going higher than all those before him, and I watched with growing alarm. I could see how white his face was and I could imagine how afraid he was.

At last he stopped and looked down. "Jump! Jump!" came the rhythmic chant of his buddies. He looked down again and I saw a quiver passed through his body. I felt so sorry for him; I almost called out to him to stop.

Then he jumped, a shrinking jump, too close to the boulders — and the inevitable happened. His body bounced from rock to rock, hit by one only to roll down to the next one. He fell and bounced, fell and bounced, and landed on the boulders in the pool. The girls began to scream hysterically, and a shudder passed through me as Eitan sank like lead into the pool of water.

We watched in eerie silence as Effy leapt up and ran to him, ordering us to call for help on his radio unit. As he pulled him out of the water, we saw that Eitan was unconscious and bleeding all over.

"He's breathing," said Effy finally. "He's breathing on his own." He then turned to take care of Eitan's injuries, and we assisted him. There was hardly a piece of skin left unscathed on his body. I expected to hear voices of remorse or stammered apologies, but there was nothing of the sort.

"He jumped like a coward, and got hurt like one," somebody mumbled behind me.

I wheeled around. "Aren't you ashamed?" I cried angrily, "You all forced him to jump, and now that he's injured you're still mocking him?"

"Look at that — Mrs. Rabbit is defending Mr. Rabbit!" someone replied. I was flooded with anger.

"You should *all* be ashamed!" I burst out. "My friends in America would never have done what you did today!" I began to cry, as my companions answered me in a cacophony of voices.

Effy shushed them. "I don't want to hear one word about what happened — yet. We'll sit and talk about it, but not now, absolutely not now!"

"What's happening with the help?" somebody asked.

"The rescue helicopter should be here any minute," Yoav said. "It's on the way."

"Great," said Effy. "Now let's get Eitan into the shade." They carried him carefully to a shady spot, where Effy patted him reassuringly and the *chevre* sat by him chatting about this and that.

I was devastated. How could friends treat a friend like that? How could Jews act like this to a fellow Jew? Didn't they understand what they had done?

We heard the loud whirling of a helicopter above us: help had arrived. The helicopter circled overhead, slowly descending and maneuvering for a better angle. We struggled through the downdraft as the door opened, and two medics let down a stretcher. Effy fastened the straps around Eitan, they pulled the cables, and Eitan was hoisted upwards and pulled inside.

"I'll go to Rambam Hospital as fast as I can, but first I'll get you all out of here," Effy told us, and all the *chevre* nodded their heads. The door closed, and the helicopter spiraled up and away.

"The fastest way out of here," said Effy, "is to finish the route. We'll do it quickly. I have to be by Eitan's side and talk to his parents."

We jumped quickly from boulder to boulder, and reached the Meshoshim pool. The valley was beautiful and refreshing, but this was not the time to admire the small streams pouring into each other in a spectacular basalt canyon. We stood on the metal bridge watching the hikers who were sliding gaily from one waterfall to the next.

"Can we do it for a while too?" asked Danny and Yoav.

"No!" said Effy in a decisive voice.

We continued to hike, until we finally reached the main road. Effy parted from us and hitched a ride. "Go to Kibbutz Dan and stay there until morning, and don't do anything stupid," he said.

The next morning we all arrived back at Ma'alei Kinneret and met Effy when he arrived too.

"Everything's okay," he told us, none too credibly. "Everything's okay. A few breaks, bruises and a little concussion, but he'll be home in a week."

"Effy," I called, running after him. "Effy, excuse me for not waiting with my questions until we talk, but...but I can't take this anymore!"

He stopped and looked at me, surprised. "What's the matter?"

"The way Eitan's friends acted shocked me. Is that how you treat a friend? I'm not even talking about how they made him jump, but *afterwards*! Not a word of remorse, or expression of pain. Don't they care? Don't they have feelings?"

"Calm down, my dear," Effy replied in his firm voice. "You don't realize that for young people here in Israel courage is of the utmost importance. Your companions will soon be soldiers, willing to risk their lives defending the country. Of course they have feelings, but in the meantime they can't admire weakness.

They have hearts just like you do, and the time will come when they'll express their feelings more easily. Believe me, I've worked with tougher kids than these."

"But I still don't understand!"

"It's not easy to explain," Effy said seriously. "You don't know how these young people have grown up, what they've seen and experienced. You don't feel it, but terror attacks and war, and the threat of war, are always with us. All of this makes our youth place a very high value on strength and courage. In such a framework, they will very quickly extend help, and even die to save a friend. But in a framework of weakness, they won't lift a finger. Do you understand?"

"I...I guess so," I stammered feebly. "But I don't agree. It seems like a weakness of its own."

"That could be..." He smiled at me. "With time, you know, you'll come to like these young people."

"I'm not so sure," I retorted. "Where I come from *everyone* helps each other in *every* situation."

Effy smiled. "Perhaps," he said quietly. "But how many of you would be willing to die in order to rescue a friend from a minefield? How many of you would rush to help a friend under fire? Think about it."

And I did.

6

"WE'RE GOING TO JERUSALEM!" EFFY'S words rang sweetly in my ears. I had been in Israel already for three-and-a- half weeks, and I had still not seen Jerusalem.

We left the kibbutz in the middle of the night on Thursday and arrived at the Wall with the Friday morning sunrise. Effy gave us a wide-ranging history lesson on the way, and told us about the exceptional survival of the Western Wall throughout the ravages of the past.

I stood and looked at it, this Wall of ancient stone. I raised my eyes and saw how the stones became smaller as they reached Heavenward. I felt an unknown strength passing from it to me. It was an uplifting feeling, full of hope and faith. I came closer, one step after another, until I could feel the stones' dampness in the early morning dew. My throat was choked with unfathomable emotion — my cheeks were wet with tears.

What was the secret of these eternal stones? What was it that brought people from all ends of the earth to come here, bend their heads, speak their innermost thoughts, silently, and push a note deep within the stones? They come to meditate, to feel…and to leave, never to forget their encounter with this eternal Wall. These stones and the radiant blue Jerusalem sky spread out above would be engraved in my heart forever.

Wars could not destroy it, nor could evil counsel. It survived, as did our People, unique and indestructible. A Wall that every Jew is drawn to, as I was, without knowing for what. People cry there, hoping for salvation. Young, toughened soldiers stand side-by-side with unfortunate people fallen on hard times, and with ordinary Jews. Women and children, the rich and poor, brides and grooms, Jews and non-Jews — all approach and touch it with trembling hands and burning hearts. What is its power?

Effy took us through the alleys of the Old City. The savor of the past mingled with the present, penetrating my consciousness. Walking through the Arab marketplace, I looked at the iron doors in their carved stone niches, the floors with their patterned paving stones, the merchandise on sale — the small wooden carved camels, the painted ceramics, the striped Bedouin rugs.

A tremor of fear passed through me at the thought that perhaps a hostile Arab was lurking in a doorway of a darkened alleyway, but Effy and the *chevre* walked confidently and chatted loudly, as if they were walking through a neighborhood of old friends. I wondered at the sight, and found it difficult to understand.

At one alley Effy turned right, and we were suddenly in the Jewish Quarter again. The alley was still narrow, but the character of the area changed immediately. The dawn was rising against my eyes and lighting the Old City.

"Here, two thousand years ago, raged the great fire which swept through the city at the destruction of the Second Temple," said Effy as he pointed to the entrance of the "Burnt House." "This area was the upper city, where the wealthy of Jerusalem then lived. This house was damaged in the fire — and it has exciting archaeological finds that raise the possibility that the family who lived here prepared the incense for the Temple."

I listened to Effy intently, but as on previous occasions when he spoke of archaeological findings that proved events mentioned in holy books or in verses from the Bible, I felt confused. I had been taught the Bible as a kind of legendary literature, folk stories that had survived along with our people. But here I was, standing in front of a building — a Jewish house! — whose archaeological remains verified the day it had burned, and this exactly paralleled the burning of the Temple, and the fire which had raged in Jerusalem. The archaeological finds themselves showed how the *Kohanim* had used stone utensils to avoid ritual impurity, and exact utensils for the preparation of spices — finds that verified this folklore!

I didn't understand how that could be — these were real events, then; real history... *my* history.

"We'll come back here when the site opens," promised Effy, as we continued on to the remains of the ancient Tiferet Israel synagogue. With his descriptions Effy painted a picture of the splendor of the place, and he told the story of the shul's dome. A little further on he pointed to stairs that went down to a kind of cellar.

"Here's the Karaite synagogue," he explained. "The Karaites are Jews who rejected the Oral Law and follow the literal interpretation of the Written Law. Do you know why it's down there?" No one knew. "They step *down* in order to pray, which is exactly the opposite of standard Jewish practice — in which synagogues were built in a high place. The Karaites interpreted the verse 'from the depths I call to You' literally, that from a deep place one is supposed to call to God!"

"Are there Karaites today?" asked Danny.

"Yes, indeed, and some of them live upstairs here," Effy replied. There are several thousand Karaites throughout all of Israel today."

"That's all?" asked Danny.

"Yes," Effy affirmed. "Whoever reads of their big battle with Rabbinic Judaism finds it difficult to believe that this is what's left of them. If they'll give us the keys to their synagogue, you'll see boxes of crumbling books in piles of dust, the last vestiges falling away by themselves."

We went on to the Churvat Rabbi Yehudah he-Chassid, usually called "the Churvah." Underneath the reconstructed arch
we heard about how his followers, who came to Eretz Yisrael in
the year 1700. We heard about the magnificent synagogue
which was built on the site he purchased, and which was destroyed by the Jordanian soldiers of the Arab Legion in 1948.
We listened tensely as Effy described, in his colorful language,
the battle for the Jewish Quarter during the 1948 War. We
heard about those who had been captured and how the residents had stood steadfast till the end.

We continued and came to the site of the mass grave which
had been dug hastily during the days of the War and which had
been transferred afterwards. We toured the Cardo marketplace,
the Byzantine shopping mall of 1500 years ago which is an extension of the main Roman road built in the first and second
centuries C.E., and saw the "broad wall" mentioned in the Book
of Kings.

Effy described with pathos the days of Nehemiah, when the
Jews who had returned from Babylonia to build the Second
Temple held a weapon in one hand and worked at construction
with the other, reading the exact description from the Bible.

Again I was amazed. Effy constantly brought proofs from
the Bible on his trips. I had been taught differently, so very differently. But Effy, I asked myself, if he knew all this, why didn't he
keep anything of our religion's precepts?

After a while I asked him: "How can it be that a Jew like you
isn't Orthodox?"

"What?" he laughed. He didn't understand the question.

"You're always telling us about archaeological finds that
prove the truth of the Bible and the Gemara and sayings of the
Sages, so how can it be that you don't keep the commandments that are written in those books?"

Effy had his answer ready. "What's the problem? I love the

Bible! Everything in it connected with history is true and fascinating. But as far as its religious rituals, well if someone wants to do all that stuff, he can, but I'm not interested."

"But how can you differentiate between the two?" I asked. "They're both written in the same place! Don't you think they're both true?"

"No problem," said Effy with a smile, as he unsheathed his pocketknife. "You see, like this —" he marked the air with a cutting motion — "the right side is wonderful history, and the left side, old fashioned rituals that aren't relevant today. What's the problem?"

* * *

The sun had risen over Jerusalem and the golden stone reflected the morning's radiant light. I saw that people were leaving their homes, many of the men wrapped in a *tallis*, walking to synagogue. *They* hadn't made a distinction between history and mitzvos! They related to the Bible as one body of truth that had been given to Moshe at Mount Sinai.

As I stood pondering this, I turned my attention back to our tour. We were standing at the Ramban's synagogue, and Effy read us the Ramban's letter to his son, which describes poignantly the desolation of Eretz Yisrael and of Jewish life in Jerusalem. Effy was enthusiastic about the Ramban's "Zionism" — that he chose to come to Eretz Yisrael despite the many hardships.

"Didn't the Ramban write a commentary on the Torah?" asked Lior.

"Yes," replied Effy, nodding.

"But you cut that out with your pocketknife," I blurted out.

Effy looked at me, surprised.

"I'm sorry," I added, and went on, "I'm just confused by the conflicting messages I'm getting on your trip."

"You don't have to apologize," said Effy. "But as for conflicting messages, I can tell you that you Reform Jews are experts!

You yourself pray on Shabbos, but you desecrate the holy day. You read the Torah, yet you don't believe in it. With me at least, I'm honest with myself."

"What you said isn't fair!" I said, rising quickly to my defense and that of my community. "We choose all that is nice and worthwhile to observe. For Shabbos, we choose prayer and the family experience."

"Aha!" replied Effy with a smile. "And *we* choose the Land of Israel and its history. And we do things on the Sabbath with our families too — we go on drives through the countryside and go to the beach. What's the difference?"

"But we don't claim that the Bible is all true, so what's wrong with choosing whatever is meaningful to us? You, on the other hand, say that it *is* true historically, but you ignore its obligations."

Effy was quiet for a moment and then shrugged. "I've never given this much thought."

"Because you have a pocketknife," I said quietly.

"Evidently," Effy returned with his bellowing laugh, "you Americans aren't equipped with that, eh?"

The discussion was over.

When we left the Old City and passed through the Damascus Gate, the sun already stood high in the sky. The sounds of peddlers and hawkers blended with the ringing of the church bells. Arabic was being spoken all around, Jewish soldiers stood guarding with their weapons ready. My eyes and ears were bombarded with contrasts and absurdities. In one instant I realized I was experiencing the complexity of Jerusalem in its many aspects.

We began to walk through Jerusalem's picturesque neighborhoods where the old and the new stood in contrast, side by side. We walked and walked: we saw Mishkenot Sha'ananim and Yemin Moshe, and we passed by the Russian Compound. We visited the old neighborhoods, the winding narrow streets of Nachlaot with their old stone houses. In the afternoon we visited the Knesset, the Israel Museum, and the Shrine of the Book. Finally we visited Yad Vashem on Mount Herzl.

By the time we arrived, exhausted, at our youth hostel we were overwhelmed with impressions and experiences. This was the first time we had "done" a city and not outdoor terrain.

"You have two hours to eat something and rest," said Effy cheerfully, "and afterwards — a surprise!" I tried to rest, but my mind reeled with so many thoughts and feelings. I was affected by the magnetism of Jerusalem, but my impressions had been so contradictory and confusing. I heard a cacophony of voices, scenes, and sounds. I tried to get some rest physically if not mentally, until I saw the hues of the Jerusalem sunset. The sun set and again, there was no dusk, no time to prepare for it — Shabbos had descended!

The things that Effy had said troubled me. Was he right? Was my Reform observance of Shabbos dishonest in some way? I put on my Shabbos clothes and then stepped out on the little balcony that faced the street. I was entranced by what I saw. Shabbos was tangible. Little boys with long *peyos*, holding their fathers' hands as they walked to synagogue together, the men in dark suits or striped robes, and some with Chasidic fur shtreimels on their heads. The tumult of traffic had ceased and the silence of Shabbos slowly spread over the streets.

I had a strong desire to go to synagogue to hear the Shabbos prayers. It was almost a month that I'd been in Israel, and I had not yet been at a Shabbos service. But I didn't want to miss Effy's surprise, which was certain to be very special. Effy announced that we were to leave immediately after supper.

A cool, pleasant breeze greeted us. "Jerusalem puts an air conditioner on every night," joked Effy. My companions sang out the words "mountain air as clear as wine," a snatch of the song "Jerusalem of Gold" which had been so popular after the Six Day War. In the sweet mountain air there was the smell of Shabbos, and tranquility washed over me.

When we reached a certain street, Effy announced, "We've reached the gates of 'Ultra-Orthodox Land.' Notice all the wall posters and their archaic style, the overcrowded streets, and the old-fashioned people here. I guarantee you interesting sights on every corner. By the way, this is the place where all the riots against 'Sabbath desecrators' take place — you've seen them on TV."

"Wow!" everyone said.

"We're now entering the neighborhood of Meah Shearim!" Effy announced dramatically. A cry of enthusiasm burst forth from the young people, and they seemed gripped by a spirit of enthusiasm.

As Effy had said, the wall posters were the first source of humor for my companions. Some of the posters called upon Jewish girls, "daughters of Israel," to dress modestly; some were to "our Jewish brethren, compassionate people who are the children of the compassionate"; others called for donations for "a widow left with ten children"; all of these drew roars of laughter as Danny and Lior read them dramatically, making comments that I couldn't understand. I was puzzled — from what I could understand, it didn't seem humorous, and although the people in the neighborhood looked different from us, still they looked like kind, good Jews.

We passed through winding alley after winding alley as Effy described the history of the area and the architecture, pointing out the inner central courtyards and the crowded enclosure, meant to protect the residents who had settled outside the walls of the Old City.

Suddenly we heard the sound of singing: a lively, heart-warming melody sung in several voices. We stopped and listened silently.

"If I'm not mistaken, those are *zemirot Shabbat*, Sabbath hymns," said Effy. "Come after me quietly, maybe we can see the family singing."

We softly, unobtrusively followed Effy until we stood next to

NOTHING BUT THE TRUTH

a large window close to the ground. "They're sitting in the light and we're standing in the dark," he whispered, "so *we* can see *them* clearly. If you get too close, though, they'll see you, so pass by one by one, and take a quick peek."

I had never peeked into someone else's house before and it seemed wrong, but I too was caught up in the excitement of the moment, which had gripped everyone. I also came forward to look when my turn came.

I looked, and stood rooted to my spot.

Someone shook me and said, "Bend down, Amy, or they'll see you!" I heard others saying "Move on," and "Let others look too," but their words didn't enter my consciousness.

My whole being was transported into the picture in front of me. There was a beautiful Shabbos table covered in a heavy embroidered white tablecloth. Silver candlesticks gleamed in the dancing flames of the candles. The table was laden with dishes. Around the table sat two older couples and at least ten children. At the head of the table sat the father, wearing a shiny dark robe, his head covered by a large, white yarmulke. His eyes were closed tightly in deep concentration and his curly *peyos* swayed to the rhythm of the melody he was singing.

Next to him sat his wife, a black headdress crowning her glowing face. At their sides sat their children, who were of all ages, adding their voices to the singing, and at the other end of the table sat a man who evidently was the grandfather. I could see only his bent back. The grandmother sat by his side, and clapped the hands of a chubby baby on her lap, to the tempo of the singing.

I stood there staring, unable to move, as my companions pushed me forward, whispering, "You're being selfish, let us see too!" I realized that this view was also dear to them, no matter how estranged they were from it.

Afterwards Effy gathered us together by the side of the narrow lane and said quietly, "Did you all have a look? That's the

Shabbos table of the *dosim*, the ultra-Orthodox. Now you know what it looks like."

"It's, um, it's really nice," said Limor hesitantly.

"I think so, too," echoed Koby. "It's too bad we can't stand there and look some more."

"Amy stood there like she was hypnotized — she didn't let anyone else look long enough," complained Danny.

"Shhh, shhh," Effy hushed them. "We'll continue to walk around, and maybe we'll see similar scenes. But please, be quiet. If they see us, the whole lovely picture will disappear."

"Why, what will happen?" whispered Omri.

Effy shrugged his shoulders. "I don't know," he said, "but they're used to violence, so it's best to be careful."

"That's hard to believe," murmured Koby.

We walked down the steep alley, hugging the stone walls, listening to the sounds and occasionally peeking in, taking pleasure in the serene scenes of these Jews, while at the same time fearing their reputed violence.

Everyone agreed that there was something magnetic about the sights and sounds. Effy hummed some of the tunes quietly to himself. I could see that he himself was enjoying the surprise that he had prepared for us!

We crossed the narrow street and turned right. Effy took us to a large stone building. "In *this* Yeshiva, you'll hear some very special singing," he told us enthusiastically. He went around the building with us in tow, to where we could stand and listen at the upper windows of the basement dining-hall.

He was right. The singing we heard was truly different, something from another world: hundreds of young men's voices, singing wonderful, yearning melodies. We stood there, close to the wall, and listened in silence.

Suddenly Danny burst out, "I'd give anything to go in there!"

"Don't you dare," warned the others. "Do you want a provocation? We're few against many."

But I couldn't picture those singing young men angry. I was sure that their faces positively radiated happiness.

Effy took us from there, almost by force, up to the Geula neighborhood. There were families with many children, all dressed in their best, walking along the streets. We looked at them as if they were from a different planet.

"Where do they hide the stones they throw?" asked Lior.

"Maybe they keep them in the wide pockets of their robes," answered Danny.

None of the people we saw seemed bothered by us being there, despite our extremely different appearance. No one turned to stare at us, aside from one old man, and he did so with a beaming face, wishing us warmly, "*Gut Shabbos.*"

That night sleep eluded me. My trip to Israel was coming to an end, the trip that I had so longed for and had been so disappointed by. It was finishing just as I was beginning to find what I had so searched for.

On that day Jerusalem etched itself deeply into my heart.

*   *   *

The day of departure arrived and like all leave-takings it wasn't easy. I had become very attached to Chana'le, and even to the young people on the kibbutz and to Effy. I had come to like them despite the great differences between us. Most of all I loved the scenes of the Land. The memories of the trips we took warmed my heart, and the magnificent view that I saw from my window all hours of the day and night stamped its impression into my heart. The terrible disappointment that I had felt during the first days, and the alienation, would demand thought and concentration — when I got home. I would have to try to understand my people and myself in a way I never had before.

For now, though, I was happy thinking about going home, eager to see my parents, my brother, and my two younger sisters again.

I MET WITH RABBI SHNEIDER THE WEEK after I returned from Israel. He wanted to discuss the Temple youth group's activities for the coming year, and of course he wanted to hear about my trip.

"Well, Amy, how was it? I'm waiting to hear!"

"To tell you the truth, Rabbi Shneider," I said quietly, "I'm still struggling to sort out my impressions." I well remembered his parting words to me: *I'm certain that you'll also be courageous enough to come and tell me your impressions even if they're negative.*

"Even so," he insisted, "tell me a little bit."

And so I told him about the Israelis on the kibbutz, about the wonderful trips guided by Effy, and even about Chana'le. But not a word did I say about my shock at discovering the complete disregard that the kibbutz members had for Jewish practice.

Rabbi Shneider listened intently. "And how about their values?" he asked.

"The young people on the kibbutz admire strength, courage, and freedom," I replied. "Other than that they seem to respect nothing."

Then I told him about the incident in Zavitan.

He shook his head. "You know, Amy, I've been trying for some time to understand the nature of Israelis. On the one hand

50

we would like to establish a strong base for our Reform congregations there. But sometimes we wonder if we will ever succeed in bridging the culture differences."

I had nothing to reply.

"And what are their feelings about religion?" he continued.

"Oh, they dislike the Orthodox, just like we do," I answered. "But —" I suddenly found myself unable to tell him about my own "feelings about religion" which had been so confusing there... those Shabbos songs and the glow on those Jewish faces, the old stone buildings, the winding lanes, were all still with me.

"But what, Amy?"

"But... but I have a lot to think about."

*   *   *

I agreed to continue working with the youth group for another year. Rabbi Shneider told me that he and the members of the Temple Board had a very high opinion of my work. "We are aware that next year will be an important one for you academically, Amy, and we appreciate your willingness to take on this responsibility as well."

"Thank you. I imagine this will be my last year with the youth group, though."

"Why?" asked Rabbi Shneider.

"Because when I'm at the university I'm going to have to devote myself exclusively to my studies," I said with a smile.

"Do you have concrete plans yet?"

"I'd like to do my first degree in economics and sociology, and then I want to study law."

"We wish you success with your big plans, my dear," said Rabbi Shneider, "but even so we won't give up on you easily."

CHANUKAH WAS DRAWING NEAR, AS WELL as Christmas. At the Temple we were beginning to organize festive parties for the children and the adults. At school I had lots of tests, and I had to navigate between my studies and the activities of the organization. In order to proceed with my academic plans, I had to finish my studies with honors.

But one day before the vacation, Mrs. Levitt, my Jewish history teacher at the Agnon school, gave a class that upset everything for me. Surely she had no idea how her words had affected me.

What did they do? Oh, Mrs. Levitt, I cried to myself, your words have put me on a path that there is no turning back from. Ever.

In another few hours I would have to answer to myself the question that Mrs. Levitt had put before us in history class: *Latkes or a fir tree? Matityahu or Nicholas?* And what was I to do, planning the impressive party that was to begin in just a few hours? What could I say? And anyway, who would want to listen to what I had to say in the midst of the festivities? Oh, Mrs. Levitt! Why couldn't you have given this class before I got myself into all this?

My mother peeked into my room. She was dressed elegantly, as usual, and my father was standing by her side knotting his tie.

"Amy," my mother said with concern, "what's the matter?"

"Dad, Mom, I can't... I think I have a fever or something like that. I...I'm sick," I stammered.

My mother rushed over to me and felt my forehead. "Oh my poor Amy, today of all days?" she lamented. "Were you so overworked? Was it all too much for you? How awful to have to miss the party after all that you did for it."

"Oh, it's all right," I protested weakly. "It doesn't matter if I'm not there."

My father suddenly looked at me suspiciously. "Amy... are you sure it's just a matter of not feeling well?"

"Yes, yes," I said with a forced smile. My pangs of conscience grew, but because of my father's suspicious look, I had to continue my performance. "Dad, could you cover me with another blanket, please, I'm shivering from the cold."

"Oh, dear!" Mother was alarmed. "I'll have to call Dr. Barnett immediately."

"Please, no," I pleaded anxiously — that was all I needed — "it's not necessary. All I need is a good night's sleep, a warm blanket, and a little bt of quiet. I'm sure it'll pass. Don't worry about me, really. And you can tell me all about if afterwards."

Dad hesitated.

"I promise to call you immediately if I feel any worse," I said.

"Okay." Mom returned to being practical. "The children are already waiting for us downstairs." They kissed me and left.

Relief washed over me. The great obstacle was behind me, but why, why was I crying now?

*   *   *

Mrs. Levitt's questions came back to me.

"I'd like to ask, which of you celebrate Chanukah? And which of you celebrate Christmas? And which of you celebrate both?"

The students from my Temple were very proud when we raised our hands to answer her questions, and I was the most proud after all the activities that I had prepared for the Temple youth group.

She listened to us, and then responded.

"I can understand," she said, "that we Jews celebrate the festival of Chanukah, and that Christians celebrate Christmas — but what I can't understand is that there are Jewish-Christians or Christian-Jews."

You could have heard a pin drop.

"Christmas is celebrated by those who believe in Christianity," she went on, "and therefore they celebrate the birth of its 'founder.' But the Jews, who, for almost two thousand years of our history were 'credited' with the birth and death of 'that man,' how can they celebrate two holidays at the same time, one — Chanukah, that has within it the victory of the Jews against Greek culture, and the other, a celebration of the birth of Christianity? Of that Christianity which has always tried to delegitimize and erase Judaism from the world? Whoever esteems Matityahu and his sons, the priests of Judaism, cannot also esteem the 'founder' of Christianity."

"Mrs. Levitt," Eric took advantage of the loud silence in the classroom. "Mrs. Levitt, I still don't understand what harm there is in eating latkes for Chanukah and getting presents for Christmas. Why can't I celebrate both holidays together?"

'If you do," said Mrs. Levitt in a determined voice, "then you're just being greedy!"

Peals of laughter were heard in the class.

Our teacher's unprecedented inflexibility caught us unprepared. When we asked about her own religious beliefs and practices, she answered sharply, "That doesn't matter. Your own opinions and religion are what should matter to you! What I'm trying to do in this lesson is to wake you up from the long hibernation you've given your brains! If you've felt a spiritual and emotional shake-up in my class — then you've made my day! But if you've *also* thought about it after class — then you've made *your* lives for yourselves."

Mrs. Levitt's lessons had always been fascinating, but this time... this time she had shaken up my world. And I asked myself, how had I not thought of this before?

At the moment I had answered her defensively that there was a harmonious blending of thought involved in celebrating the two holidays together, words that I had of course drawn from Rabbi Shneider's lively sermons.

"Really, Amy!" Mrs. Levitt replied angrily. "I expect a bit more intelligence from you. Where, throughout history, was there ever such agreement between Christians and Jews? During the Middle Ages? The Crusades? The expulsion from Spain? The Inquisition? The blood libels? Or the opposite, with Yehudah the Karaite? The Via Dolorosa?"

Now, as I lay in my bed thinking of her words, my cheeks still burned with shame. I was the one who had worked so hard to prepare tonight's program, a "winter festival" combining the two holidays and inviting Christian youth. I had combined menorahs with Christmas trees, presents from Santa Claus had been placed in stockings, and dreidels had been stuffed with "Chanukah presents." Santa Claus himself was due to make an appearance! The tables were laid impressively — a small decorated fir tree in the center of each table surrounded by platters of latkes. On the dais there was a huge menorah.

But now Chanukah was strangled within me, and Christmas was not my holiday. Mrs. Levitt's voice of truth tortured me and sent me into my bed. I tried to cover my shame with my blanket. How much time passed I didn't know.

Suddenly I heard the front door open and close and then the sound of footsteps approaching. I wrapped the blanket more tightly around myself. My mother came anxiously into my room. "Amy, sweetheart, how are you feeling?"

"Much better, Mom. How was it?"

"Oh, wonderful, wonderful," she said enthusiastically. "Everyone was so impressed by your work, Amy. Rabbi Shneider didn't stop praising you and the children got up and said how wonderful it was that even though you were in the midst of exams, you still devoted time and energy to ensuring the success of the festivities. And your group's performance was exceptional in its message of unity — Rabbi Shneider even announced that because of its success, he would recommend that it be performed for a wider audience — perhaps for a gathering in church this Sunday night.

"Amy!" my mother cried. "What's the matter? Steve, call Dr. Barnett!"

"No, Mom, don't call him. I'm all right. I just felt nauseous suddenly."

I tried to sit up in my bed. On my night table my mother had placed a small, decorated fir tree and next to it a plate of latkes. My feeling of revulsion intensified.

"Mom, could you...could you please move that stuff away from here?"

My mother's eyes widened in surprise.

"I think the smell of the latkes is making me nauseous," I said apologetically.

She quickly took the latkes off and placed them far from me, leaving on my night table only the little Christmas tree! The nausea I felt became real distress, so I got up and rushed to the bathroom.

"What do you say about this illness?" I heard my father ask my mother.

"What's there to say?" answered my mother, sighing. "What a shame it happened now."

"You didn't understand me," said Dad. "I mean, do you think it's real?"

"What?" Mom replied. "How can you think otherwise?"

Dad was quiet. "Did you see the expression on Amy's face when she saw that tree and the plate of latkes next to it? She looked as if she'd received a blow."

"It was because of the smell!"

"I have a feeling it was because of the *tree*." I heard my father's thoughtful voice.

"Do you remember," Dad asked softly, "the Christmas when Amy was six? At the Christmas-Chanukah party, when she received that big doll from Rabbi Shneider?"

"Yes."

"Do you remember why she got it?"

"No, I don't... but why are you remembering that now?"

"Because the way she looked this evening reminded me of the expression on her face that same Christmas. I remember, when Rabbi Shneider asked, 'Dear children, who is giving us presents tonight?' Amy stood up on the tips of her toes and answered in a clear voice..."

I heard Mom's laugh. "Yes, I remember! She said... Matityahu!"

"Yes, and everyone laughed and Rabbi Shneider raised her on his shoulders and said, 'You're bright, very bright, and you've actually reminded us that we should light the Chanukah candles first, and *then* receive our presents from grandfather Claus, right?'"

"'No,' she said, 'we get presents from grandfather Matityahu.'"

"Yes," Mom laughed again. "Do you remember what Rabbi Shneider said to us then? He said, 'From her stubbornness one would think that your daughter Amy comes from an Orthodox home!'"

They both laughed as I continued to listen by the wall.

"In my opinion," Dad said, "she has always objected to Christian symbols."

"Oh, you're exaggerating," said my mother. "Don't forget,

she's the one who designed all the decorations for the interfaith winter holiday program tonight!"

I breathed deeply. The feeling of nausea had passed. I returned to my bed surprised, encouraged, consoled by the fact that in my childhood I had been smarter.

 I WAS SITTING IN THE LIVING ROOM TAKING advantage of the long winter break to review the material for my history exam when my brother Tony walked in. His gait was strange, and a quick glance at him awakened a feeling of anxiety.

"Tony, is everything all right?" I asked, worried. He didn't even look my way, but went on with strange steps to climb the stairs. Ever since he had come home from university for semester break I had discerned a change in him. I tried to talk about it with my mother, but she didn't want to hear. "Since when have you become a tale-bearer, Amy?" she asked me.

"What do you mean a tale-bearer?" I was hurt to the quick. "You know how precious Tony is to me, but I feel that something's happened to him."

"Don't be silly," she hushed me. "He's away at university, far from home. That's all. It's hard for him."

I didn't agree with her. Tony went out all the time, and when he came home he closed himself in his room. My formerly cheerful brother was now withdrawn and introverted, and had a strange expression on his face. How could my mother not see all this?

When I'd tried to talk to him, he evaded my question with all kinds of excuses. But tonight it looked as if something was really wrong. Suddenly the sound of a thud came from the direction of the staircase. I jumped up and ran to him. He was sitting on the floor, dazed. When he saw me he stood up shakily, and said angrily, "What do you want from me, pest?"

He had never spoken to me like that before. We had always been close, despite the differences in our personalities. What had happened to him? He tottered a bit, and looked as if he was going to fall again. Then he went to his room.

I followed him and knocked on his door. "Tony, Tony, open up," I pleaded.

Tony finally opened the door and stood there with an awful look in his eyes.

"Tony, what's happened to you?" I asked, frightened.

"Shut up," he answered, trying to push me back.

Revolting alcohol vapors hit my face forcefully, and in a flash of understanding I cried out, "Have you been drinking?"

Then Tony slammed the door. I sat there stunned and shocked. This was not my big brother who was so close to me. This was someone else, frightening and strange.

What could I do? My mother didn't want to see it. Oh God, please help Tony! I cried, and then I broke into sobs. When I heard father's car in front of the house, I decided what to do.

"Hello, Dad," I greeted him.

"What's the matter, Amy?" He lifted my chin and looked into my eyes. I whispered one word: "Tony."

"Tony?"

"Yes. Don't you think he's been acting strangely the past few weeks?"

"I do think so. But what's happened? Tell me."

"I tried to talk to him today. He yelled at me, and when he slammed his door in my face, I very clearly smelled alcohol."

My father looked troubled. "I hope that you haven't said anything to Mom."

"I tried to talk to her about it, but..."

My father caught my arm firmly. "Please don't do that again!"

I was taken aback by the tone of his voice, but he went on, "I don't want your mother hearing upsetting things like this from you."

"She doesn't *hear*, even when I tell her," I mumbled.

My father spoke sharply. "What your mother is or isn't interested in hearing is none of your business at all. Your business is to treat her with respect. And my job is to let your mother experience the good things, and the bad I take on my own shoulders — they're wide enough to take a lot."

I nodded my head.

My father bent over and lifted my chin. "Look, Amy, you and I are cut from the same cloth. When we encounter a problem, we immediately tackle it, and sometimes we even get hurt, right? Your mother is different. When she sees something negative, she prefers to ignore it rather than deal with it. That's her way of coping. And, you know, people like that often get by without the blows that people like you and I get. But sometimes, if I think it's dangerous for her to be this way, I help her, without trying to convince her and without claiming that she's made a mistake. Do you understand?"

He took my hand. "As for Tony, I'll take care of the matter. And as for you, keep quiet."

I thought about the things that my father had told me. Actually, with a few words he had clarified a lot in my childhood, things that had always bothered me — why Mom acted like that, and why Dad never pointed out her mistakes to her, but did the opposite. The more I thought about it, the more I understood and accepted what he said.

People have the right to cope with life however they want. I wondered, though, how my father would deal with Tony's new path. That night I didn't hear Dad exchange a word with him, but in the morning I discovered to my surprise two packed suitcases in the hall, and next to them lay Dad's and Tony's fishing equipment.

"What's this?" I asked, amazed.

"Tony and I are going on vacation for a week," Dad announced casually.

"He's so lucky!" said my sisters Debbie and Linda jealously. They loved camping trips with the family. Tony himself sat silently in the corner with a forced smile on his face, trying with all his might not to meet my glance. When they left, we waved good-bye to them and wished them a wonderful time.

My father had chosen a clever and painless way to deal with Tony: outside the house, and in a framework of an enjoyable vacation. I was proud of him, but I was still hesitant about the results.

My mother looked more rested and calm, and I understood that my father had removed the worry my words had given her.

The week passed quickly and soon we were expecting them back. Mom prepared a festive meal, and Debbie and Linda went out to buy a bouquet of flowers. I had decided to prepare a different kind of surprise for Tony. His room was always full of disorder and mess. Mother had tried tens if not hundreds of times to change the situation, but it hadn't helped, even though he was always pleased when she made order.

Then she'd changed gears, and told Tony, "The room is yours and so is the mess. I'm not going to send my maid in there, and I'm not going to clean it myself." And that was how it would stay for many days, until Tony himself despaired from the mess and the long and tiring searches and would arrange things a little. Then the cycle would repeat itself.

I decided to welcome him by making his arrival a "new beginning" for him in an original way. I worked for many hours straightening up his mess, sorting and putting all his clothes, books, and odds and ends in their places, and throwing away the garbage. I made notes of where his various possessions were to be found. After three mornings of concerted effort, the room was ready — in perfect order, sparkling clean and ventilated. Debbie and Linda couldn't believe their eyes, and hurried to tell Mom, who came running up the stairs to see for herself this wonder.

"Unbelievable!" she said several times. "How did you do it?" she hugged me happily. I felt then that both of us had overcome the obstacle that Tony had placed in front of us. "I just hope that he keeps it like this," my mother said, expressing the hope of all of us.

Dad and Tony came home tanned and happy, with no cloud darkening Tony's brow. Tony had returned to being the big brother I knew and loved. The atmosphere in the house was relaxed and cheerful, and together they described their fishing adventures to us.

Tony dozed off in the armchair in the living room, and later went into his own room. He immediately came out stunned, and when he could speak, the emotion in his voice testified to his happiness. I presented him with the updated list of his belongings, and where they could be found, and he thanked me warmly.

"Amy, I'll never forget that you did this for me," he said, brushing away a tear that appeared in the corner of his eye. After a moment's pause he said, "I owe you an apology too. I acted very badly towards you that night. It's hard to explain to you, but I've been under great social strain for a long time. I've gone to so many parties this year where my friends drank and I stubbornly refused to join them — my college friends and also my old friends from here — but this time they teased me to the point that I had to prove myself. I know it sounds stupid, but in the situation I found myself in, I felt there was no choice. When I came home, I was still under the influence of all that..." His face contorted. "I couldn't look myself in the eye, and then all of a sudden *you* started to ask questions, and it was just too much for me. Do you understand?" Before I could answer, he added, "You probably don't, because you're a natural leader, not a follower like me. You're so strong you probably don't understand how social pressure can work."

"Oh, but I do," I murmured softly, as the image of Eitan jumping and landing on the rocks rose before my eyes. I told Tony about it, and he was silent.

"Until you go through it," he said finally, "you don't believe that you're such a weakling. But I'm fortunate," he said. "I have wonderful parents and a wonderful sister."

*   *   *

I cornered my father at the first opportunity. "What did you do to him, Dad?"

"I convinced him that everything depended on him. That even under great social pressure, a person has his inner strength, and doesn't have to give in. We talked a lot, and analyzed it all from every possible angle. Tony came to understand that he did have control over such situations, and that his capitulation was ultimately his personal choice. I think," he added, "I really helped him to realize that a person can have control even in a situation like that. He was depressed about his failure, and about his general weakness in social settings. I tried to explain to him that his feelings and behavior are normal, but that being aware of them helps in coping."

"Do you think he'll succeed next time?" I asked.

My father sighed. "To tell you the truth, I'm really not sure. The youth of today isn't like it once was. I'm going to keep my hand on the pulse. Tony *is* a strong boy, but in order to cope with everything he sees he'd have to be made of steel. At any rate, I'm considering transferring him to another university, a more competitive one where he'll have to work harder in order to succeed — where the students can't spend so much time on all the nonsense that his friends are filling their heads with now."

"We'll really have to encourage him," I said quietly.

"For sure," Dad agreed. "And you've made a good beginning. What you did with his room improved his feelings about himself. You see, Amy, positive acts can accomplish a lot more than criticism."

MY PERSONAL STRUGGLES WITH VALUES and Judaism got pushed aside as all my energies were invested in my exams and my work with the youth group. Now I was about to do something I'd been waiting for since my trip to Israel — visiting the concentration camps in Poland. Every year a group of Jewish students from my town had joined the "Journey of Life" trips but I had never joined. It hadn't meant anything to me before I met Chana'le.

My mother was one of the biggest opponents of the idea. "Why do they have to expose young people to such a depressing thing?" she said repeatedly to my father, but he held the opposite opinion.

"Historically and morally it's an important part of Jewish history, and it can't be ignored," he would explain.

"So she can study it in university — why should they take tender young people there?"

The argument would come up every year when the registration forms for the trip arrived. Every year my mother's opinion won out because I also wasn't interested in going. This year, though, I knew that my father's opinion would win out, because we would present a united front. I so much wanted to see for myself the places that I had heard about from Chana'le.

This year it was decided, on the initiative of Mrs. Levitt, who accompanied the trip to Poland every year, to enrich the students' knowledge of the Holocaust before they reached Poland. She approached Rabbi Shneider, and explained that because of the pupils' poor knowledge of the Holocaust, they were not deriving the maximum benefit from the trip. He agreed to finance the course on condition that the classes be given at the Temple and be open to the general public, not just to those going on the trip.

The classes began. Mrs. Levitt taught many of them, but she also brought other lecturers. Some of them were eyewitnesses who had survived; others were professors and researchers on the subject of the Holocaust. Treasures from the Holocaust Museum were brought, members of organizations for perpetuating the memory of the six million came, and even a representative from the Second Generation organization spoke to us about the problems of children of the survivors and of the third generation as well.

The classes were wonderful, and the participants couldn't stop praising them. My father was sorry that his work prevented him from coming, but he asked me to update him about them, which I did willingly.

One evening as we were sitting down to supper, my mother was serving the potatoes when my father asked me, "What was there today?"

"Oh, I got a real shock today," I answered.

"You say that after every class," said Dad with a smile.

"Well, it was even more so today," I explained. "Today we saw a film which wasn't exactly a documentary, but was nevertheless interesting. It was an exact reconstruction made on the basis of the proceedings of the Wansee Conference and on testimony taken at the Nuremberg trials. All the documentary material collected from the conference was incorporated into a film staged in the same place where it happened, and in exactly the same amount of time, 90 minutes."

"If I'm not mistaken, this was the conference which decided on mass extermination," said Dad.

"No, that's a common mistake," I said knowledgeably. "This meeting was called to discuss how to implement the decision, and they decided to perfect the mass extermination, and to involve the civil ministries in it also."

"Who made the film?"

"The Germans," I replied.

"Really?" Dad was surprised.

"Yes, it was during Adenauer's time, when the Germans were trying to prove that there was 'another Germany' besides the Nazis. They chose actors who closely resembled Eichmann, Himmler, Heydrich and all the rest. They reconstructed every detail exactly. But what was the most shocking," I said, "was the atmosphere before and after the horrible decisions. They chatted, drank, and laughed as if it was a friendly party. It was simply horrifying."

"What exactly did they decide there?" asked Dad, as he served himself hot potatoes.

"Eichmann was then a young officer, and they give him the task of carrying out the trial destruction in Chelmno with gas trucks. Himmler presented the problem to Heydrich — you understand, Dad, Eichmann is shown as a young, sensitive officer, which was how he tried to present himself, and Himmler is trying to explain to Heydrich that the experiment in Chelmno was too difficult for Eichmann. The exhaust gas from the trucks was not deadly enough," I went on matter-of-factly, "so that when the bodies were taken out they continued to convulse, and Eichmann vomited from the scene."

I heard a gasp.

"Please! Enough!" fulminated my mother. "Do the two of you think that it's possible to eat like this?"

Dad and I looked at each other. "I'm sorry, Sue," he said sincerely. "I didn't even realize that I was eating."

"I can imagine," said Mom. "How can you eat with all these terrible descriptions?"

"Sue, please forgive me," my father apologized, "and you, Amy," he said, turning to me, "from today there will be no talk about the course at mealtime."

I nodded my head, embarrassed that I had upset my mother so much.

*   *   *

The day of our departure arrived. The buses packed with young people arrived at the airport, where we were directed to the waiting planes. Unlike other flights that I had been on, this time I felt great tension. Our country of destination was a huge cemetery containing a sizeable portion of my people, and I was supposed to land there and try to feel the horror, in order to be able to eternalize it within me and to learn to pass it on to the next generation.

Fog met us when we landed at the Warsaw airport, and the buses took us straight to the hotels. I looked out at the streets as we drove, and in my mind's eye I saw masses of Jews being kicked and pushed, torn from their warm homes with their meager bundles on their shoulders. Old people, women and children marched in front of me in a procession of darkness.

As I rode through the clean, empty streets, I could envision peeking from every side the sorrowful eyes of my fellow Jews being taken away. Eyes tortured and hungry, hurting from a nameless pain. I watched people leisurely doing their shopping, talking of this and that, smiling and continuing to live their lives as their fathers' crimes and injustices rose in black clouds to the sky.

Every day we went on long excursions by bus, for hours and hours, until we had seen with our own eyes the desolate hills, and those green from human fertilizer. I remember arriving at Maidanek on the second day of our trip. The weather was somber, and a strong cold wind was blowing. We stood at the top of an exposed hill opposite a monument of ashes, shivering.

A sharp wind blew, and the cold penetrated through to our bones. In our mind's eye we saw our brethren returning and arising from somewhere, standing in endless rows, their bodies exposed to the cold. Beaten with whips, trampled and tread upon with nailed boots, degraded and starving, they were here now, standing and trembling.

I raise my eyes. The skies are gray, gloomy, full of human smoke. I lower my eyes to the ground; here are corpses and blood; the air becomes too heavy to breathe. I look around myself and there is fear in all eyes. There are those who cry, finding relief in tears, but not consolation. There are others who tighten their lips, trying not to cry. And some think of revenge.

But within me there is nothing but an awful emptiness. Suddenly beyond the fog I hear singing, tearful and choked: *Ani ma'amin, b'emunah sheleimah* — "I believe, with perfect faith..." Those precious words, recited for generations — hope, belief? Is that the answer in this valley of death?

A short, older woman walks with slow steps toward the microphone.

"I am Ethel the daughter of Pinchas and Sarah Leibovitz. I am standing here on this cursed ground that swallowed millions of tortured, suffering, and starving bodies. Ground that quaked when it silently absorbed the spilled blood of my parents, my brothers and my sisters. Soil that was trampled down by the feet of bestial men.

"I stand here today on this soil, and underneath this sky, the last witnesses of my loved ones. There are those who say 'cursed is the ground' and others who say 'cursed are the skies'; and I say: cursed is man!

"Cursed is the man who remained silent when he saw thousands of trains sealed with human victims. Cursed is the man who witnessed it and breathed human smoke and was silent.

Cursed is the man who could have opened his hand to help but instead closed it. Cursed is the man who saw piles of skeletons bleaching in the sun and was silent. Cursed is the man whose silence allowed them to continue to slaughter without mercy.

"Where were all the free countries who met in Evian and signed our fate with the agreement of silence, a silence of weakness? Cursed are they, cursed forever!"

Ethel fell silent, and the youth orchestra began to play. Representatives of the youth delegations from all over the world spoke briefly, but I was no longer listening.

We got to Auschwitz on Thursday. We looked at the wooden sign with its grotesque motto "Labor Makes One Free," at the long wooden barracks, at the barbed-wire fence, at the watchtowers. Everything — almost everything — was as it had been then. The silence of death was all around. I looked at the broad horizons that had been strangled by the wood and iron works of human hands.

The image of a man came between the heavens and the earth, between freedom and death, a man who wore white gloves while he tortured, starved, abased, and murdered millions of human beings with awesome precision and monstrous order, a man who built gas chambers and crematoria, who made a sea of ashes and dug countless mass graves. If it is not within the power of culture and intelligence, order and discipline to restrain bestiality, if those only serve to sharpen its claws and whet its fangs, what, then, can imbue man with humaneness and compassion?

At Auschwitz and Birkenau we were greeted by a stone gate opened wide, through which wound dozens of railway tracks, tracks which carried millions of victims to their death.

If I were to imagine a picture of hell, its gate would not be different from that of Auschwitz or Birkenau. The clatter of trains roars in my ears and the screams of victims are heard... suddenly the image of the young Chana'le rises before my eyes,

Daniel in her arms. She is standing here next to the track, clasping her son close. "Water," her parched lips whisper. And here is the *mussulman*, the prisoner holding out thin arms to grab her baby away from her. I hear her cries and see her sink to the ground as her child is given into the hands of others — old hands, whose fate has been sealed.

Trembling overtakes me, and I search for something to hold on to or I will collapse like the masses of my brothers and sisters on the track. With fear I walk forward, the sound of my shoes ominous on the tracks. How terrible is this place.

About the jumble of prosthetics, the heaps of eyeglasses, the mountains of shoes, the hair...about the yellow-green gas stains that made the very stones into testimony, I cannot write. There is nothing to write...and if there is...it is impossible.

 FRIDAY IN WARSAW, JUST A SHORT WHILE before Shabbos. I look out of my window at the bustling city, and see before my eyes thousands of Jews who once were but are no longer. Here they hurried to buy their Sabbath necessities; there Jewish children, washed and fresh, played happily in the courtyards of the buildings. My eyes scan the streets and squares — perhaps I will see one Jew, maybe one little boy all ready for the Sabbath. But no; there is not one. They have all been erased.

The setting sun fills the sky with streaks of blood, and the last light of day is buried in darkness and black smoke.

"Shabbos," I whisper to myself, and break away from the window. Almost mechanically I make the last-minute preparations, because in a minute or two the Sabbath will be here.

Perhaps we were the only Jews to keep the Sabbath here, to cease our weekday labors, since the very lives of those Jews ceased...and perhaps together with the thousands of young men and women who have come here from all over the world to create a memorial, a living monument, in the midst of matter and spirit, we will gain wisdom and learn in the course of time to command our children with feeling and pain, "You shall not forget!"

We convened in the hotel's large convention hall. Everyone

arrived as if on command, and the young people filling the hall resembled each other, their white shirts all gleamed, and a light radiated from everyone's faces — a light that I had not seen before.

No one had asked us to come dressed this way, but even so the hall was packed with snowy whiteness. I also wore a white blouse — because of a feeling in my heart. Was that what had happened to the others too? When the Sabbath prayers began, everyone — Jewish youth from all over the world, religious, non-religious, Reform and Conservative — joined in with fervor.

Yarmulkes appeared from somewhere, as one after another trembling hand placed this Jewish symbol, forgotten for some time, upon their heads. For me, and for the others as well, it seemed, it was praying from a different world — with no organ as in the Reform Temple in Lakeside, and no professional choir, but there was an uplifting of the spirit, a unity which flowed with the singing of *Lecha Dodi*. It was a singing of the soul, which burst forth from deep within the innermost spirit. It was full of pride and joy. I looked around me and saw that, like me, many were wiping away tears. Those who didn't know what prayer was, looked through the Siddur, a little embarrassed, but they also sang with the same fervor and the same feeling, kindled from that Jewish spark that is never extinguished.

*   *   *

On the following Sunday evening, our last night, Mrs. Sarig, one of the teachers accompanying the Israeli delegation, announced that young people who spoke English and who were interested in meeting a contingent of German youth were invited to meet at the entrance of the hotel at 8:45 P.M. They would go to a discotheque together. When this was announced, Mrs. Levitt jumped up from her seat as if she'd been bitten by a snake! With forceful steps she approached Mrs. Sarig. "What are you talking about?" she demanded.

"The matter wasn't brought to your attention?" returned Mrs. Sarig.

"No, it was not!"

"I'm sorry," said Mrs. Sarig, "but in Israel it was decided that in addition to the traditional trip to the concentration camps there would be an opportunity for a social get-together between Jewish and German youth. The Ministry of Education decided that the meeting would be optional."

"Very nice," said Mrs. Levitt in a voice as cold as ice, "and you want to tell me that you are going to go to this meeting?"

"Yes, certainly," replied Mrs. Sarig. "Those are the directives."

"I wouldn't accept such directives!"

Mrs. Sarig turned towards the exit. "I'll go with whoever wants to join me. Whoever doesn't want to, doesn't have to."

"No one from my group will join, do you understand?" said Mrs. Levitt. "If I were in your place, I wouldn't go."

Mrs. Sarig's face turned red: "Please stop lecturing me on morals! A person who chooses to live in the fleshpots of the Diaspora has no right to say what Jewish youth should or should not do — especially to a Zionist like myself."

"A Zionist?" Mrs. Levitt raised her voice inquiringly. "And what kind of Zionism is it that brings Jewish children to a discotheque with Germans?"

"A Zionism that believes in peace, friendship, and security, and ultimately in erasing the hostility that has characterized our history," Mrs. Sarig replied. "Dialogue is the key."

"Dialogue! Do you think that the Jews who were turned into ashes didn't speak with their Polish and German neighbors? That they didn't have "peace" and "friendship" with them? Yet that didn't prevent the Germans from exterminating them in clouds of smoke.

"And besides that," added Mrs. Levitt, "you should know that love of Zion is not dependent only on where you live. Have you never heard of the importance of Jewish education in the Diaspora?"

A tense silence prevailed in the hall for a short moment, and then the argument between Mrs. Levitt and Mrs. Sarig developed into a general polemic. The non-religious youth from the Israeli delegation gathered in the entranceway, while we looked at them with mixed feelings. Some security men and Mrs. Sarig accompanied them to the meeting. Watching them leave, I felt troubled: who was right?

I watched as a gray-haired man who had accompanied us on the trip got up to speak to Mrs. Levitt. "I am convinced," he began, "that all those remaining here feel shaken, some more and some less. But surely all are asking how we could possibly meet and "have fun" with a group of German youth after all that we have seen here!"

The man, who spoke with an unmistakable German accent, was silent for a moment and then continued, turning to address us. "For me, it is almost a trauma to see such a disgraceful action. For nine years I have regularly accompanied the youth groups on the "Journey of Life" visits. I have always spoken with them about my experiences as a Holocaust survivor, and I answer questions and describe the life that we led before Hitler rose to power. However, the story that I am about to tell you I have never yet told in public. It is a story that changed my life completely and the strong impression it made on me is even stronger after what we saw here just a few minutes ago."

Absolute silence reigned in the hall.

"My name is Eddie Klein. I was born and raised in Berlin, where my father was a cardiologist and my mother was a well-known pianist. But my story actually begins with my grandfather, who was also a doctor. During the First World War, he served in the German army, and three times he risked his life to save his German comrades — two officers and a commander who had been wounded in battle. The last one he carried on his back for a long distance in order to join up with the retreating forces. On the way, he was shot and seriously injured, but he continued to carry the commander on his back until they reached a military camp near the center of the German forces, and there his strength gave out. He was hospitalized, went through several operations, and remained partially disabled.

"Grandfather received three medals of honor at the end of the war, and he would wear them at every festive occasion in which he took part.

"I remember, as a small boy, the special place in the living room that was reserved for Grandfather's medals of honor. They lay on a special pedestal in the carved, wooden sideboard. Grandfather would say to me, 'You see, Eddie...' here he would become choked up with emotion, '...that's what it means to be a soldier, to lose blood for our German homeland.'

"Grandfather was a successful doctor, but most of his pride was for his wartime experiences. He always argued that if only all the Jews would be like him then anti-Semitism would disappear. Jews who are different in their dress and behavior arouse the wrath of the Germans, and rightly so, he said. The Germans must understand that we are like them, part of them, and then they will stop hating us. Grandfather preached intentional cultural assimilation, and spoke about it often. This was how he educated his children.

"My father continued in his path, also becoming a successful and learned doctor, who settled into German culture very well."

Eddie Klein was quiet as he looked at us. "This was the kind of house that I grew up in, and this is exactly what I absorbed. The message was: 'If we become Germans more than Jews, the Germans will forget our Jewishness.' But the truth..." his voice dropped, "the truth is that *we* forgot our Jewishness and *they* forgot our German-ness! When the Nazis came to power, Grandfather assumed that it would only be for a very short time, for it wasn't possible that the Germans would allow such a government in their enlightened country.

"But as time went on, the tension in the street grew and my father began to speak about emigrating to Switzerland. Grandfather reprimanded him: 'What's happened to you, son? With me there is nothing to be afraid of — my house is a "city of refuge." No one would dare to harm a German soldier with three medals of honor.' Father agreed with him, and we moved to Grandfather's beautiful villa."

Eddie Klein mopped his perspiring brow and continued.

"We lived with Grandfather for several months. Life was uneventful until one day the front door burst open and SS soldiers came in. My grandfather stood and saluted them! Their response: they laughed wildly and one of them kicked Grandfather in his stomach.

"Grandfather bent over with pain but then straightened himself and said with dignity, 'Evidently you do not know with whom you are speaking, my friend. I was a German soldier in the Great War, and these are the medals of valor I received.' He pointed with wounded pride to the medals of honor that lay on the carved sideboard.

"'German soldier? Filthy Jew!' screamed the SS soldiers. They grabbed the medals and ribbons and destroyed them in front of Grandfather's eyes.

"'I will report you to your seniors,' he said with courage. 'I will not allow such wild behavior in my house to pass in silence.'

"They responded to Grandfather's courage with murderous blows. When my father tried to defend his father, they beat him cruelly also. 'Out! Out!' they screamed at us, and shoved us out into the street, beaten and stunned. Father managed to limp along despite the blows he had received — but Grandfather, we found out, didn't get up again.

"We were sent to the east with thousands of other Jews, but our situation was worse than theirs. We had no belongings with us — so sure had we been of Grandfather's immunity that we had not prepared anything for the evil day, as others had! Aside from the clothes on our backs we left all that we owned and loved behind."

Eddie Klein sighed. "My grandfather believed in the German culture, and we believed in him. And what were we left with? Dust and ashes. My father and I were our family's sole survivors. Several days after the camps were liberated, he died from typhus. I was left alone.

"Thousands of times I've asked myself, Why didn't they act logically? Why didn't we emigrate to Switzerland? Why did Grandfather rely on his medals of honor when outside all was terror? I have found only one answer: my family's esteem for the Germans was so overriding that they were certain that the 'enlightened' German culture wouldn't permit injustice.

"I myself despise that culture and all that stems from it. I cannot understand those who are prepared to establish financial and social ties with Germany. I cannot understand those who send that which is dearer than anything to us, our youth, to dance and 'have fun' with the grandchildren of murderers."

He was silent. We were all silent. "For me," he went on, "to see *our* generation going out to socialize with *theirs*, is like seeing my grandfather come out of his grave and kiss the German medals of honor."

In my hotel room I tried to sleep, tossing from side to side, going over my thoughts again and again. Two years had passed since I had decided to deepen my ties to Judaism, but the education I had received and the habits of my life had returned me to the unchanging banality of my life. I had traveled to Israel; I had felt Jerusalem, and I had met Chana'le — and Lena. I had returned with a decision to deepen my acquaintance with history and Judaism, but what had I done since then? I had vacillated, struggled, and essentially remained the same. Chanukah had so troubled me, and the discussions with Rabbi Shneider, the preparatory studies for this trip, and the meeting of last Shabbos. Would I just return home, go to my room, and forget again?

I would have to change something. Eddie Klein's story brought home to me just how far things could go without Jewish values. I didn't want to be like Eddie Klein's grandfather! I want to be connected with authentic Judaism; I didn't know much about it, but I so wanted to know more.

The dawn rose and broke, and I had not slept at all. "Dear God," I cried from my heart, my head buried deep in the pillow, "light my way to You! I can't find it alone. Give me the strength and the courage to do it."

I got up quietly and opened the window. A gust of cool air burst in, and I looked up at the skies above the city. They always remained the same, I thought, but the city below changes constantly. Streets, stores, vehicles, all are in a continuous dynamic. Man changes his environment without pause, but is afraid to change himself. The cold wind whipped my face, but I continued to look within myself as I looked out of the window. Everything was spread before me — the skies that don't change and the city that constantly does, and the "I" that wants to reach the sky but is planted, ever so deeply, within the earth.

"I have to change," I said suddenly, out loud. If I've reached the conclusion that Judaism has made us the different nation that we are and has given us the supra-natural ability to survive, then I must deepen my acquaintance with it. "And if Shabbos gives my spirit tranquility and meaning," I whispered to myself, "then I must keep Shabbos."

I closed the window slowly, and returned to my bed.

The decision was behind me.

 DURING THE ENTIRE FLIGHT HOME ONE thought consumed me: How would I hold to my decision to keep Shabbos? At that stage I knew very little about Sabbath observance, but even so I was determined to keep what I did know, with all my strength. The question was how to do it.

I decided that in the first stage I wouldn't involve my parents; they would certainly show immediate opposition, and that would make it more difficult for me. Therefore I decided to avoid Shabbos desecration by inventing all sorts of excuses and pretexts. Then either they would understand by themselves, or a suitable opportunity would arise for me to bring it up with them.

*   *   *

On my first morning back home, I went shopping in the housewares and electrical stores, searching for a Shabbos hot-plate.

"We don't have anything like that," the salespeople told me over and over again. I realized I would have to go to an Orthodox neighborhood, but that would have to wait till next week.

I made other plans. On Tuesday night, as I was getting ready to wash the supper dishes, I took a small plastic container and put leftover pieces of fish and potatoes into it. I closed it well and put it as far into the refrigerator as I could, trying to hide it behind a jar of jam. That would be one Shabbos meal.

An undertaking as simple as organizing cooked food for Shabbos was almost impossible in a home like mine! My mother believed in fresh, and not processed, foods. She didn't use canned goods or frozen food either. Unlike her contemporaries, she cooked real meals regularly, and she did it gracefully. A maid helped with the cleaning up, and my mother cooked in her free time. She also didn't believe in leftovers, and because of that she was careful to cook small and quite exact amounts; all leftovers were thrown away.

I didn't know how I was going to sit down at the Shabbos table with leftover food from Monday, Tuesday, and Wednesday on my plate — but what I did know for certain was that I didn't have a hotplate, and that I couldn't eat my mother's food because it was cooked on Shabbos.

Thursday night I repeated the previous night's maneuver, and hid another small container with leftover chicken and peas in the refrigerator.

On Friday afternoon, I was in my room when I heard terrible screams coming from the direction of the kitchen. I ran quickly down the stairs expecting to see a fire or some other emergency — and I was surprised to find the kitchen clean and straightened, with no sign of smoke or trouble! There was only my mother standing next to the open refrigerator, looking shocked.

She gave me a penetrating look. "Is this what that Holocaust trip did to you?" she asked, pointing to the containers of leftovers. "You've come home a Holocaust survivor, storing bits of food? Oh, I knew that I shouldn't have let you join that awful thing!" She turned to my father, who had come into the room. "What do you say about Amy's disgusting behavior?"

My father didn't say a word but sent me a look that asked, "What do *you* have to say?"

I kept quiet. The last thing I could say under the circumstances was, "I'm saving the food because I've decided to observe Shabbos"! My mother threw my precious leftovers into the garbage can, and poured enough soap and water on the containers to scrub the entire kitchen.

"Amy," my father said quietly but determinedly, "I demand an explanation."

"I kept the food for another purpose," I replied quietly.

My father raised his eyebrows. "May I know what?"

Only a few hours were left before Shabbos came in, and I didn't have too many choices, so I decided to simply tell the truth.

"I've taken it upon myself to observe Shabbos, and because it's forbidden to eat food that's been cooked on Shabbos I saved these remains." There! I'd done it! I looked at my father and saw that he was sighing with relief.

With my mother, the opposite occurred. "So not only did you come back from there a Holocaust survivor," she fumed, "but an Orthodox one as well!"

I understood that I could only tell the truth, and it was a relief. "Mom, I experienced such an amazing and wonderful Shabbos there that all I wanted to do was to re-create it here, without trying to keep you or Dad from conducting your Shabbos the way you want to. I didn't want to be a nuisance to you. Why are you so angry?"

"Thank you," my mother replied sarcastically, "for taking us into consideration and deciding not to interfere with how we conduct our Shabbos!"

"We'll discuss the Shabbos on Shabbos," said my father, putting an end to the discussion.

I went up to my room and began my Shabbos preparations, trying vainly to believe that it would be as beautiful and meaningful as the last one. I spread a white tablecloth on the corner table, took two pretty candles and a pair of simple glass candlesticks out of my handbag, and placed them in the middle of the table. I also took out two small rolls that were to serve as challos, covering them with a flowered napkin. A small bottle of kiddush wine and a china goblet completed the picture. I turned on the night-light so that I wouldn't have to turn it on during Shabbos. Then I went into the closet and chose a white blouse and a blue skirt, the same clothing I had worn the previous Shabbos. The day had begun to decline.

With a trembling hand I took the matches and lit the candles, covered my eyes, and said the blessing — for the first time in my life. Many flames appeared in front of my eyes, and hundreds of pure white shirts. It seemed like only yesterday that we had brought in the Shabbos Queen in the Warsaw hotel.

I sat down on my rocking chair with a prayer book in my hand, trying to reconstruct the melody of *Lecha Dodi* from the previous Shabbos, when I heard a light knock on the door. My father came in. For a moment he stood still and stared. The small table was a touching sight. It seemed to radiate the warmth of Shabbos. My father came over to me, visibly moved.

"Amy," he asked gently, "do you want to tell me about your decision?"

I began to tell him about my experiences from the previous Shabbos, but my father found it difficult to understand what had so moved me, what the prayer there could have had that the prayer in our Temple didn't have. I found it difficult to explain to him. Maybe more authenticity, I explained. It was just more *Jewish*.

"More Jewish than what?" asked my father.

"More Jewish than the prayer in Temple," I answered without hesitation. "You know, Dad, the Temple sometimes seems more like a church than a synagogue."

My father looked at me. "And why is it important to you to be more 'Jewish'?" he asked again.

"Because I *am* Jewish," I said. "And after I understood what the Germans did to our people, it seemed awful to try to be like non-Jews. I would prefer to be like the Orthodox Jews!"

My father began to pace silently back and forth in the room, and then suddenly he stopped and asked, "When did you really begin to think about the whole matter of Judaism?"

"I guess last year, when I was in Israel."

"If so, then Rabbi Shneider was right," said my father. "But you didn't try to change things then. What happened now?"

"I think I went through a certain process, something matured in me during my encounter with the Holocaust, with all its aspects and ramifications. My Jewish identity that had been awakened during my trip to Israel was simply strengthened. I feel at peace with myself like this, Dad."

My father nodded, looking troubled. "I must tell you that I hope this is nothing more than a passing phase," he said, "because if it isn't, I don't know how we'll be able to live together."

I could hear the pain in his quiet words.

"I can only warn you not to pull the rope too tight," he went on. "Otherwise you will be losing the most precious relationship that a girl can have — closeness with her mother."

He was right. I also felt that my relationship with my mother was threatened, and that the tension had been rising between us during the last two years.

"Your mother is especially sensitive to the issue of religion," he went on. "She can't accept the lifestyle of the Orthodox. She actually detests it. I hope that you will weigh your steps logically, Amy, and judge for yourself if it is all worthwhile."

I loved my mother deeply, and I had such pleasant memories of my childhood. I didn't want to harm my relationship with her, but I knew that my father was right. I wouldn't be able to live with my mother if I was Orthodox; the whole idea was impossible. Deep within myself I longed to come closer to religion. My short encounters with it had etched the sweet taste of its holiness in me more than anything else I had ever experienced. But I knew that each step that took me closer to Judaism was distancing me from my mother, and the delicate and precious thread that bound us together could be broken.

My father left the room, and I was filled with melancholy, that even the glowing Shabbos candles could not succeed in dispersing. I opened my prayer book, trying again to sing the moving melody of *Lecha Dodi* that I had heard in the "valley of the shadow of death." I hummed it quietly trying to quench the thirst of my soul by remembering the sweet waters of the past Shabbos.

Linda knocked on my door, and came into the room. "Mom and Dad are calling you to come down to eat." Her eyes widened with surprise when she saw the table. "What's that?"

"That is a Jewish Shabbos table."

She frowned. "And our table isn't a Shabbos table? It isn't Jewish?"

"Not really, Linda," I said, feeling confused myself.

I took her hand in mine, and didn't say anything more. We went downstairs together. I still didn't know what I was going to do.

My father poured wine into his glass goblet and stood, smiling. "Here, my dear Amy, I've decided on a compromise: I'll make a proper Kiddush for you, and you'll eat the wonderful Shabbos food that your mother has prepared."

I was still standing there dumbfounded when my father began to recite the Kiddush in a clear and sure voice. "*Yom ha-shishi* ... and God blessed the day ... and sanctified it." The words rang in my ears, with their simple meaning that allowed no compromise. God blessed the Shabbos, so how could I desecrate it?

"I'd be happier, Dad, if you didn't force me to eat any of the cooked food." I didn't look at my mother.

He flushed. "You know, I once heard of an old Jewish saying: 'Without good manners, there is no Torah.' And you, Amy, don't have good manners."

Tears filled my eyes. I washed my hands for bread, and said

the blessing in a whisper. Then I put some lettuce salad and cole slaw on my plate. We ate in silence, only the clinking of the silverware impinged on the terrible quiet.

My mother brought two steamy platters to the table that smelled especially delicious. I wasn't planning to eat any of it, because I knew that my mother was still cooking the food after Shabbos had already come in. She served everyone meat and pasta, but ignored me completely.

"This is really exceptionally delicious," Tony said, while giving me a kick under the table.

"It's really even more delicious than ever," chimed in Linda, sending a meaningful look in my direction.

"A delicacy," summed up my father with satisfaction. My mother smiled; more than anything she loved my father's compliments, and they were honest.

"Can I have Amy's portion?" asked Tony defiantly.

"Certainly," said my mother, "if she agrees." I nodded my head. Tony went on eating with obvious pleasure. Was my embarrassment giving him satisfaction? A lump rose in my throat.

Later, when we were going upstairs, he whispered, "Amy, I did that on purpose. If Mom would have had to throw away your portion, she would have been even more angry with you."

"Thanks," I said, "but you didn't have to kick me if your intentions were so pure."

"The kick was for your decision to be Orthodox, and the rest was good intentions. But Dad is right, Amy — you don't have manners."

Dejected, I went to bed. I had so much wanted a different kind of Shabbos.

In the morning everyone drove to the Temple while I stayed at home. I said the morning Shabbos prayers, made Kiddush for myself, and ate the roll with vegetables. It wasn't exactly Shabbos cholent, but it also wasn't Shabbos desecration.

I didn't join the rest of them in the afternoon when they went to Woodland Park. For us it had become almost a tradition to drive there every Saturday and to enjoy the wonderful view, ride bikes around the pond, play tennis, practice golf, or have a swim in the pool. All of us were members of the country club there, and every Shabbos we had good times.

I can't say that I didn't want to join them, but I felt that to keep half of Shabbos or a third or a quarter meant not keeping it at all. I well remembered the uplift in spirit that had I felt at the true Shabbos the week before, so even if I had to sacrifice a certain pleasure for that, it was worthwhile.

Shabbos passed by very slowly, and when I saw the stars in the sky I breathed a sigh of relief. It had been a very lonely Shabbos. I made *Havdalah* just as my family was climbing the stairs, and thus ended my first battle for Shabbos.

*   *   *

For the next three years, I struggled to keep Shabbos. It was always difficult, and my parents' resolve to show me understanding and tolerance threatened to explode.

THE SOFT SNOWFLAKES WHICH BEGAN TO pile up in the street became consolidated into huge drifts, almost completely blocking the entrance to the gray and gloomy institution where I had begun to volunteer, as a sociology student, during my second year in college. Yesterday I had gone through the list of children's names, and pointed randomly at one: Terry Brown. Tomorrow I would know if my choice was a successful one for me and for him, or maybe even for both of us together. When all was said and done, I wanted to complement my sociology studies with something real for the benefit of someone who could use it.

As I waited in the green office. I wondered why it was that so many educational institutions painted their walls green; some people claimed that it was a soothing color, perhaps because of the green of nature, of grass and leaves. But I had never felt soothed by green walls.

No calm or pleasantness emanated from the office that had been allocated for our meeting. Perhaps it was because the heavy table that divided the room into half formed a kind of barrier between care-giver and care-receiver. Or perhaps it was because of the old dusty pictures on the wall hung on wobbly nails, that swayed with every breeze. Or the dried potted plant that sat on the windowsill and had long since exhausted its energies in yearning for a drop of water. I leaned on the bookshelf but the cloud of dust that settled on my sleeve made me flee back to the "barrier." Apparently the books as well had not received the touch of a human hand for quite some time.

I sat and waited, and then he came into the room. Actually he burst in like a storm, looked at me with a sneer and said, "Okay, here I am."

I felt that those words were really saying, "I'd love to fly away from here." I studied him: a 14-year-old boy, really a child, a very thin child. His blond hair fell over his gray eyes, but didn't succeed in concealing the impudent and scornful expression in those eyes. Something about his face hinted at struggles that usually are not the lot of a child his age.

"Hey, are you just going to keep quiet and look at me the whole time?" he asked, shifting his weight from leg to leg and grinning at me.

"No," I replied. "Let's talk a bit."

His face twisted and he looked away. "All right...okay... Whada'ya want to talk about? My parents? Or maybe the problems I had when I was young, and how I became a..." he pronounced the words with scorn, "a habitual offender? Or maybe you want to talk about the weather, or maybe about the white snow? Huh?"

I laughed. He knew all the usual opening gambits. He had already learned a bit too much about life, I could see.

"We won't talk about any of those things," I said. "Let's talk about friends. Do you want to?"

"Friends? You must mean the guys I 'work' for, right?"

I was silent.

"Okay, so it's like this. I go into the street dressed in clothes that are torn, and with the most innocent face I can put on, and go up to a commercial van that's parked near the sidewalk with the windows closed. The driver is sitting at the steering wheel, usually waiting for someone. Then I start to nag him to give me some money. I try to get him to feel sorry for me. I don't leave him alone till he opens the window, and exactly at that moment my 'friend' comes out from nowhere, puts his quick hand inside, opens the door and threatens the driver with a pistol. More than that I really don't know, because at that moment I pick up my legs and fly out of there. I don't want them to get me mixed up with the whole thing. It's as if by chance the guy took advantage of the moment that he opened the window. But I know," he said after a short silence, "what they do. They take him with the truck and the merchandise he has in it to a certain place and there they empty out everything. They tie him to a chair and then disappear. And until he gets himself loose and succeeds in contacting the police, there isn't anything to look for... and that's it!"

I was astounded by the freedom with which he spoke about his terrible dealings — he didn't even try to hide his actions.

"Terry," I asked, "do you... *like* this, um, work?"

He laughed. "After I get the dollars, sure! Before? No!"

"And is it worthwhile?" I continued.

"Look, if you make thirty dollars for five minutes it's very worthwhile. And I don't really have to work for it."

"Except to steal a bit," I replied.

"Me? Whada'ya mean? I don't steal, they do — I help them a bit, but *I* don't steal anything. Hey, you're not writing anything down, are you?" he asked suddenly.

"No, I didn't come for that, Terry. I came only to talk to you."

He grinned. "Okay."

"And what do you do with the money?"

"It all goes for food and cigarettes."

"Are you hungry?" I asked. "Don't you get enough to eat?"

"Nah, nothing like that. There's plenty. It's just that I like to earn my own money."

The conversation with this boy fascinated me. On the one hand he made such clever observations; but on the other hand, issues of morality didn't touch him. How could this be?

"Terry, if I arranged a part-time job for you, let's say as a messenger or something like that, with a regular salary, would you stop doing this 'work'?"

"Maybe," he said, "but for sure I'd look for another way to earn more on the side."

"Why?" I asked. "Surely you don't *want* to steal if you don't have to."

"Tell me," said Terry with a mocking smile, "doesn't our President have his hand in the government till? And government officials don't steal from public funds and private corporations? You think the principal of this school doesn't steal phone conversations and stuff like that? You think storekeepers don't steal by adding things up wrong, and cleaning people don't steal cleaning materials? Everyone steals! So they can have more. It's just that there are thieves who wear suits and ties and look elegant, and thieves who look kind of rotten."

I was shocked. Who had instilled such ideas in him? I realized that Terry wasn't an ordinary thief; he was a thief with an ideology and role models!

"Who taught you all these things that you're telling me?"

"You want to know who was my best teacher?"

I nodded.

"The *New York Times*!" He laughed; he saw he had succeeded in utterly surprising me. "Every day there are reports on all the thieves, all the types that I told you about."

"So even if you had a lot of money, you'd continue to steal?"

"I think so," he said, "but if I was really rich then I'd be a different kind of thief, like those elegant ones. I'd even ask lawyers how to steal legally," he said with a grin.

He didn't let me get a word in edgewise.

"There is such a thing, you know. I read about it in the *New York Times*. There was a story there about someone called Nancy Schultz, who came out innocent due to lack of evidence

— she'd stolen $50,000! Did you see the article in yesterday's paper?"

I shook my head.

This was definitely enough for my first meeting! I had a lot to think about. In time I discovered that Terry came from a middle-class family, had gone to a regular school and had even excelled, until the fourth grade. Then he had become friendly with street gangs and began to decline. There was no clear event in his history that I could point to with certainty as the one that dragged him to the street. He hadn't grown up in poverty, his parents were normal, he had a good head for studies — so what pulled him to the fringes? Today at the age of fourteen he had no motivation to change his present situation.

I discussed this puzzle with my mother: How could I convince a boy like Terry that honesty was an important value, and logically necessary for the survival of a regular society, and that stealing was a disgraceful thing? His nature apparently didn't feel that; it wasn't important what the reasons were. In his immediate surroundings he saw the opposite. And those people who were supposed to serve as role models, those who were the elite, were exactly the ones who used the most devious means to reach those very same ends. How would it be possible, therefore, to convince him to adopt a value like honesty? By quoting the law? But law didn't particularly impress him.

My mother was of the opinion that individuals like this boy simply didn't understand truth, that he had been born with a fundamental flaw, like a genetic defect. The lack of any inborn moral sense would of necessity drag him to crime. But I didn't agree with her; Terry had shown me (with the help of his "good teacher") that people who had been honest, or who had at least been so for long periods in their lives, in the end turned to stealing, that everyone was a thief sooner or later. We discussed the matter together but didn't come to a definite conclusion.

I knew well that no explanation I might give to Terry would

leave its impression on him when he thought he needed more cash. And really, maybe there was no force in the world that could stamp "Don't steal!" For when one is estranged from the Master of the World, Who gives everything to everyone, perhaps there is no reason why a person shouldn't take from whomever he can.

THE FINAL EXAMS OF MY SECOND YEAR IN college were behind me. I took leave of my friends and returned home. I was homesick for my room, for the warmth of home, for my father, mother, Tony, Debbie and Linda. It had been almost a month since I had seen them. The pleasant smell of baking and cooking greeted me, the sweet smell of apple cake.

After the kisses and the familiar questions I went upstairs to my room, taking a few minutes to arrange my belongings, then went back downstairs. I was surprised to see the table set for an out-of-the-ordinary festivity.

I saw porcelain plates, crystal glasses, delicate cloth napkins; long wax candles were set in the middle, and next to them stood a flower vase filled with red and white roses. The sight was too elegant to suppose that it was for my homecoming.

"Are we having guests?" I asked.

My mother nodded her head in affirmation. "Very honored guests." She smiled happily.

Now I felt real curiosity. "Who are they?"

My mother looked at me as if weighing what to say, and then finally she smiled brightly and said with emphasis, "Tony is bringing us his fiancée today. And her parents."

I cried out in surprise. What exciting news! I kissed my mother and wished her *mazal tov* warmly.

"Who's the girl?" I asked. "Do I know her?"

"Jean Rogers," she answered.

"Jean Rogers?" I echoed. "The one I knew in high school?"

"That's right, Jean Rogers," said my mother, probing me with her eyes. I felt my heart catch in my throat, but forced myself to swallow again to ask the next question.

"Did she convert?" I asked anxiously.

"No!" answered Mother in a definitive voice. "They decided to get married with each one remaining in his own religion."

"Oh, no!" I cried. I felt the blood leaving my face, and I uttered my next words without weighing them beforehand, just from the shock and the pain.

"Weren't there enough Jewish girls? He had to pick *her*?"

"What are you talking about?" Mother answered in anger.

My heart was bursting from pain. "A Jew decides to marry a non-Jew, and we're going to celebrate?"

"Yes! For us it is an occasion to celebrate," she replied coldly. "Jean is an accomplished young lady, and the fact that she isn't Jewish doesn't detract at all from her value in our eyes. We're not racists like you! And if you don't want to partake in our happiness, then nobody will force you to, but please... there is one thing I will hold you to, as long as you are living in this house," Mom went on, the hurt evident in her voice. "You will not put a damper on our happy occasion! You have permission to stay in your room."

She waved her hand, signaling to me to go upstairs. I understood that the suggestion was the most comfortable one for us both, and so I started to climb up the stairs, holding back tears. "Does Dad also feel the same way about this matter?" I stammered somehow, turning around for a moment.

"Certainly," said Mom. "If you think that you will find a partner in this house for your crazy racism, for the outmoded ideas of an ancient Judaism, then you are in for a crushing disappointment. And now I don't want to hear another word from you," she said, turning to the kitchen.

I ran to my room, opened the door, and burst into tears. This was not how I had pictured my return home! I asked myself why they had waited for my return, and why they had kept me in the dark right until today! Two opposite and confusing actions.

Truth to tell, Jean really was an intelligent and gentle young woman. She played the piano well, and I remembered her pleasant personality from parties and other activities in high school. I had nothing against her at all — I liked her, in fact — but she wasn't part of my people, and my brother would not have a Jewish home.

Was it possible to call a deep feeling of identity with my people "racism"? All that I wanted was that my brother, like every Jew, would continue the glorious heritage of our people and not assimilate into another nation. Was this racism?

Was my brother's action truly an act of disloyalty to his people and his God? Why was I so distressed? This phenomenon was not so unusual in our congregation, I told myself. Many people we knew had married non-Jews, and no one regarded it as wrong. But in my drawing closer to tradition, I simply saw it with different eyes.

But any thinking person knows that intermarriage is a sure way to destroy the Jewish nation, I told myself. But what have you done about that? I asked immediately. My inner voice mocked me: *nothing, nothing at all. You went to those weddings and bought presents and acted as if everything was fine. What happened now? Did lightning strike your brother?*

I stood by the window, angry and hurt; there was truth in what my inner voice was saying. This was how we were educated, and we had received permission if not even encouragement to do this. Rabbi Shneider had spoken many times about a synthesis between the monotheistic religions in a future age, and the end of isolationism. In fact this was his explanation of the verse, "The wolf will lie down with the lamb."

But you hoped that it would never happen to you, right? my inner voice continued.

A car's headlights approaching our driveway caught my eye. I saw Tony come out first dressed in an elegant jacket and slacks; he looked happy. I saw how he helped Jean get out of the car, and she also looked elegant and happy. My father, looking content and satisfied, led Jean's parents to our house.

My mother was right: Dad didn't look at all concerned, quite the opposite in fact. Everyone walked towards the door, smiling. I looked at them, and their happiness hurt me very much. But I wondered, did I have the right to destroy this happiness on the strength of my Jewish identity?

Stupid, stupid! another voice was quick to protest. Theirs is only an imagined happiness. What is the value of a bond made on the basis of disloyalty? How can someone for whom the values of nation and religion are not binding be faithful to the marriage relationship?

Who says that you're right? Another voice countered. Have you examined this idea?

The tempest of voices and emotions within me didn't abate. The louder the voices of laughter and happiness became downstairs, the more confused I became. I knew that intermarriage was forbidden, but I didn't have the necessary tools to cope with the situation.

Suddenly an idea popped into my head. I sat down resolutely at my desk and began to write the following letter:

Dear Rabbi,
I am turning to you because of the emotional distress that I am suffering. I grew up as a member of a Reform congregation and received a very liberal, pluralistic education. During the last two years I have taken the first steps towards studying Jewish thought and keeping some mitzvos.

Recently my brother became engaged to a non-Jewish woman and they have agreed that each side will keep its own religion and in their home they will have a parallel celebration of Jewish and Christian holidays.

I understand that my brother's action is destructive, and that he is actually severing himself and his children-to-be from their Jewish identity. On the other hand, however, I know that this marriage is bringing him great happiness, and that it is a direct result of the kind of education we received. Is it right and desirable for me to get involved in the matter, and try to convince him to cancel the engagement? Or should I just stand by and not interfere?

My parents argue that Judaism's stand on the matter is racist, but can it really be true that guarding one's national identity is tantamount to racism?

I would appreciate it if you could answer these questions for me, and if you could instruct me how to act in these circumstances. Also, what would you advise my brother to do in this situation?

Thanking you in advance,
Amy Gellman

I made three copies of the letter. The first I sent to Rabbi Ben Hur, a Reform rabbi in Jerusalem; the second went to Rabbi Shein, a Conservative rabbi in New York; and the third I sent to Rabbi Katz, an Orthodox rabbi in Boro Park.

I'll wait for their answers, I said to myself. Maybe they will enlighten me with useful advice. After I had sealed the envelopes I realized that the voices downstairs had stopped completely. My family was escorting the honored guests to their car. I quickly turned away from the window so that they wouldn't see me, and listened to the leave-takings.

What will happen now? I asked myself.

It was close to midnight when I heard the echo of steps approaching my room, then silence, and two light knocks on the door. "Come in," I said.

My brother stood there, still wearing his nice suit, his eyes resting on me. He didn't speak, but looked at me with pain and wonder. I looked away and was silent. He sat down and asked,

"Amy, why did you do this?"

I found it difficult to answer.

"You can't imagine how important this evening was to me," he said. "Your behavior hurt me very much." He added, almost in a whisper, "We were always such good friends."

I nodded my head. I couldn't speak.

"Why did you hurt me on the happiest day of my life?"

"You don't understand, Tony?" I whispered. "You really don't understand?"

"You expect me to understand why my beloved sister would close herself up in her room on the night of my engagement instead of joining me in my happiness?"

He really didn't understand, and worse than that, I realized that he wasn't capable of understanding.

"You're right, you won't be able to understand me," I said in a low voice.

He laughed a little: "First you ask me if I understand, and then you tell me that I can't understand?"

I tried to choose my words carefully. "Tony," I said, "Jean is not Jewish, and if you marry her, your children and mine will belong to two different peoples! Can you understand how awful this step is that you're taking?"

"No, I don't understand," he said. "Why are you so agitated about this? Your children and mine will study at Agnon, just like we did, and afterwards they'll go to college. They'll go to Temple, they'll speak English, and they'll like potato chips, just like we did. For recreation they'll go to the country club and swim, just like we did. So how will my children be different from yours?"

I sighed. "That's what I meant when I said that you wouldn't be able to understand. You can't understand the meaning of the step that you're taking. It looks so simple and natural, but it's a move that decides fates. Jean is a Christian. They always... tortured us, the Jews. Do you understand what it is that your children will, in actuality, be Christians?"

"My children won't be Christians!" protested Tony vehe-
mently. "Jean says that even though she is a Christian, our children will be brought up like we were, in an atmosphere of
tolerance and pluralism. We'll celebrate Jewish and Christian
holidays together."

"That's impossible," I broke into his words.

"Didn't we grow up like that?" he asked.

"Unfortunately, yes," I said in a low voice, "but at least in the
midst of all the confusion we knew that we were Jews. Your children will know that their mother is Christian and their father is
Jewish. They will have to choose, because they won't be able to
take both paths."

"Listen, Amy, it could be that my children will have some
sort of identity problem, but am I supposed to sacrifice my personal happiness for that? Jean is the most perfect girl I've ever
met. She's intelligent and elegant, pleasant and sensitive. And
the main thing is that she infuses me with belief in myself above
and beyond what... anyone else ever gave me. With support like
hers I feel more confident than I have ever felt. She's exactly
what I need, and you want me to sacrifice all that because
maybe my children will have an identity problem?"

"If you think that's the only problem then you're mistaken," I
said. "You yourself won't find peace if your children are suffering
because of you. And more than that, you are actually cutting
yourself off from your own people. You're cutting off your roots,
and even if the trunk now seems secure, one day in the future it
can wither and I...," I added sadly, "your sister who loves you
and wants only your good, can't be happy if the step you are taking will bring you loss and pain in the future."

Tony looked away. "Amy, the trunk is strong and good, and
if I've cut off some roots, it will grow new and better ones. Your
words are not convincing me of anything. In fact, they're beginning to make me angry. If you can bring me arguments that are

stronger than my love for Jean, then I will listen to you. If not, then you go your way and I'll go mine."

How could I explain to a Jew who lived like a non-Jew that it was dangerous for him to marry a non-Jewish woman? They were so similar, what could possibly deter him from such a step?

"Tony," I said, "do you remember when we read that biography of Einstein?"

He turned back to me, surprised by my new tactic.

"Do you remember the part in the book about his first marriage?"

"Yes," he said, and suddenly a flash of understanding lit up his eyes. "So what?"

"I just want you to remember — he also came from an assimilated background, and his values were those of science and culture, instead of Judaism. He was also in a position like yours, and someone also tried to prevent him from carrying out his plan. In his case it was his father, in yours it's your sister. His father also didn't succeed in using arguments that were stronger than those of love, and the end — you know."

Tony paled slightly; I could feel the memory floating up into his mind. We had talked about it together at length, and Tony had been very angry at the suffering caused to someone whom he admired so much.

"So what?" said Tony finally. "What happened to him does not necessarily have to happen to me."

"He wasn't any less smart than you," I said, "and he also didn't understand how awful the step was that he took. He didn't even correctly understand the tragedies that befell him afterwards. He thought that it was just a failed marriage, when in actuality his two sons turned their backs on him forever and grew up as Christians for all intents and purposes. His wife demanded the entire sum of the Nobel Prize that he had won before she would consent to a divorce. He was left lonely and forsaken. In the end he married one of his Jewish relatives, something that he could have done many years before, and maybe he could even have had Jewish children, which didn't happen afterwards."

Tony got up from his place, gave me a quick look and said, "Amy, I didn't know Einstein's wife, but I do know Jean and she wouldn't do that, I assure you."

I looked at him. What was he asking from me, really? Only to join in his happiness. And what was I giving him in return? Words that, for him, lacked any meaning.

"Tony," I said gently, "I want to share your happiness, but I can't. I've just recently begun to understand how distorted and incorrect was the world that we grew up in. It's not your fault, but you are about to take one of the most forbidden steps in Judaism. And because I care about you, I can't share your happiness. Try to understand me, Tony."

"My dear sister, I've been trying to understand you for a long time now — without much success," said Tony with a sad smile. "I accepted all the changes in you even though they were very strange to me, but you're refusing to accept *me* as I am even though I haven't really changed at all."

He was right. I was confused.

"So you won't accept Jean as a sister?" he asked me in a trembling voice.

I couldn't answer him.

*   *   *

Rabbi Aryeh Ben Hur
The Tikva Congregation
Jerusalem

To Miss Amy Gellman,
I have read your letter, and let me assure you that I understand your feelings. Permit me to advise you by way of a similar story in which I

was asked to take part. An Israeli kibbutz member was preparing to marry a German Christian woman, and asked me to participate in a marriage ceremony involving both religions. I refused. I told him that under no circumstances would I be prepared to do so.

I myself prepared a letter to Rabbi Joseph Glazer, vice president of the Union of Progressive Rabbis in the United States, telling him the details of the case and asking him for advice.[*] I wrote to Rabbi Glazer because I thought, in my innocence, that although I am a rabbi and there was a conflict here between the good of the couple and that of the Jewish people, that the priority was the good of the couple. Originally, I was going to try to bring it about, therefore, that one of them would change their religion to that of the other — even if that meant the Jewish people would lose one soul.

My opinion was that it was better that, whatever the couple decided to do, that they not remain each in his own religion. From my experience in such cases, to live together but separately in everything that is related to religion simply doesn't work.

It isn't possible to go to synagogue on Yom Kippur and to church on Christmas, to say nothing of the problems that would arise with the children. My consideration in such cases is that if the young man is Jewish, his children won't be Jewish anyway, unless they convert. Therefore for the unity of the couple I think it's best that one partner assume the religion of the other.

The Jew, even if he changes his mind, can always return to Judaism. On the other hand, if the girl is Jewish...her way back to Judaism, as well as that of her children, will always be open if they so choose.

That is my advice to your brother.

As for you, your opinion in any case will not change their de-

---

[*] AUTHOR'S NOTE: Rabbi Glazer's answer to the above couple was: "They are simply engaging in romantic illusions that are perhaps pleasant to think about now, but have no hold on reality if looked at realistically." (This letter was copied exactly [except for the italicized section] from an official circular put out by the Rabbinic Center of the Reform in New Jersey, and was published in the Ha'aretz newspaper on June 21, 1985. It was brought to the author's attention and use by the generosity of Manof in the pamphlet "The Reform," page 53.

cision. Therefore, try not to interfere with their plans. You can present my ideas to them as a suggestion, but not more than that.

Wishing you all the best,
Rabbi Aryeh Ben Hur

I finished reading the letter and tried to think about what Rabbi Ben Hur had said. Was he advising me to convince my brother to become a Christian? How could that be?

I turned the letter over in my hand, refusing to believe that this was an answer from a rabbi, and even more than that, from a rabbi in Israel! I crushed the letter in my hand angrily and threw it away. The wastebasket would be an appropriate place for its accursed advice.

With trembling hands I opened the envelope from Rabbi Shein, the Conservative Rabbi. Who knows what he will tell me to do, I asked myself with trepidation.

Dear Miss Gellman,
Shalom to you!

Your letter touched my heart, but as a Conservative rabbi my answer to your painful question is a simple and painful one: There is no solution!

If your parents and brother are members of a Reform synagogue, then there is no chance that they will change their minds about your brother's wife-to-be going through a conversion process. As you probably know, non-Jews are not accepted as members of our congregations. Our rabbis are forbidden to officiate at their weddings, and they are not buried in our congregation's cemetery sections. On the other hand, they are allowed to take part in religious ceremonies that are connected with their children. Despite this policy, the percentage of mixed marriages in our community in the last few years has reached 42%!

If this is the result *we* have achieved, then how much more so it must be with the Reform! Not long ago I had the opportunity to see a study conducted by the Jewish Federation in which it was found that for every Jew who marries another Jew in the Reform community there are two Jews who marry non-Jews. This fact is correct for the year 1985 and onwards.

As such, your brother's action is unavoidable and you must accept it as that. I don't know if this information will comfort you, but 45% of all these marriages end in divorce.[*]

With best wishes,
Rabbi Shmuel Shein

When the reply from the Orthodox rabbi arrived, I opened the letter with a certain hopelessness, but with curiosity. This letter was handwritten and spread over four pages. I looked with amazement at the neat handwriting; did the Rabbi himself write this?

I began to read.

Dear Miss Gellman,
Shalom and Brachah!

As a Jew, I was sorry to receive your letter, because it is a sad and authentic description of the condition of Judaism in America. Your questions, like your pain, are the heritage of many of our brothers and sisters.

It is almost impossible to correct this perversion, to "straighten" this instance of "that which is crooked" (*Koheles* 1:15). This is mainly because the "patient" himself is not aware that he has contracted a "malignant disease" — so how could he give his agreement to such painful "medical treatment"? However, as a Rav, it is my responsibility to try to clarify the questions that you asked in your letter.

Jewish identity is not like the patriotic feelings of other nations. Patriotic feeling has its source in selfhood, an extension of the self to cover the loyalty of the individual to the people or the country to which he belongs because they are "his" and because he belongs

---

[*] AUTHOR'S NOTE: These figures were also published in the pamphlet "The Reform," pp. 73–75, and 80. Permission to publish them was kindly allowed by *Manof*.

to "them." But Jewish identity is something that has value incomparably greater than a feeling of belonging to a people or to a region of land, because even without the people or the land we must remain loyal to it. Judaism is an eternal bond between the Jewish People and the Holy One, Blessed be He. For this reason, even a Jew who is in a remote desert, out of contact with other members of his people, and certainly out of his country, must still remain loyal to his Jewish identity, that is, to the yoke of Torah and mitzvos that he received from the Creator at Sinai.

I assume that as you have come closer to Judaism's roots you have come into contact with the spiritual riches of our people, riches for which many of our brothers literally gave their lives in order to keep, through all conditions and situations. This is something that no other nation can claim, even if they are exiled also! Thus, a Jew who denies his identity and tries to lose it is worse than a citizen who is a traitor to his homeland. If that same citizen chose to alienate himself from his people and his country and decided to pitch his tent in an arid desert, and he then claimed that he had no identity and therefore no civil responsibility, it would be difficult to have any claims against him, and certainly not that he was a traitor.

A Jew, however, bears his Jewishness in his body and soul and cannot separate himself from it even by cutting off his limbs!

Because of this, marriage between a Jew and someone from a different nation is an attempt to sever oneself from the Source of existence itself, and not from an external source like nation or country.

There is no doubt that the gravity with which Judaism regards this bears no similarity at all to racism. What makes such marriages invalid is not that the non-Jew is unfit to join Hashem's heritage, or because his country or homeland are different from ours, or because the shape of his head is unlike ours, or because of the color of his skin and other such things. The reason is that he is lacking something in his spiritual capacity, without which he cannot be numbered as part of Hashem's Chosen People.

This can be changed, however. If that same non-Jew honestly wishes to convert, that is, to take upon himself the yoke of Torah and mitzvos, then his status is essentially the same as a Jew from birth. The very fact that this possibility exists refutes the essence of the "racism" argument. It would be very worthwhile to bring your parents' attention to the fact that it is so-called "racist" ancient Judaism which accepted into its fold great people from other nations, including those who had previously been enemies.

Ruth the convert was the daughter of Eglon, king of Moab. She became the mother of the kingdom of the House of David and the mother of the Messiah of Israel.

Shemayah and Avtalyon, one of the famous "pairs" of Sages, were Sennacherib's grandsons, and they led the people of Israel as heads of the Sanhedrin.

Onkelos the convert was the nephew of the evil Titus, but he converted and his translation of the Torah remains an essential part of Judaism to this day.

Rabbi Akiva was the son of converts, and was the conveyor of the Oral Torah.

Rabbi Meir was a descendant of converts, and every *mishnah* whose source is not cited is attributed to him.

These and many others prove that Judaism sees in every person the image of God. This is so even when the person remains a non-Jew, who is intended to reach spiritual completeness by keeping the Seven Mitzvos of the descendants of Noah.

However, if his soul wants to join the Jewish People, and he takes upon himself the yoke of Torah and mitzvos, then he becomes a Jew...

Regarding your question about your brother's marriage — I am very sorry, but it does not seem that any involvement on your part in the present situation would be able to amend or change years of education and social conventions. Your brother doesn't at all feel the fatefulness of his action, because he has never learned to recognize fundamental Judaism. He has never encountered the spiritual capability that we have carried with us since we became a people. Someone who carries nothing on his back will not feel that he has lost his baggage in the middle of the way.

It hurts me anew each time to discover what "enlightened" Judaism has done to our people. Limbs are severed from the body of our nation in such an awful manner that no one sees the blood flowing from the stump.

It is your responsibility to try and awaken your brother's conscience. First and foremost, however, you must inform him what Judaism is, but you must do so with intelligence, sensitivity, and much prayer.

From the depths of my heart I hope that in the same way you discovered the light of Judaism, so too will all your family return to their eternal and pure roots — soon.

> Binyamin Katz
> Rav, Boro Park Congregation
> New York

P.S. If you need explanatory material on any subject in Judaism, I will be happy to send it to you.

I put this letter down with great relief: This was an answer! And he's right, I told myself — my brother doesn't feel at all that he lost his baggage in the middle of the way, because he never carried it on his back in the first place.

I realized clearly now that Tony wasn't capable of hearing anything from me. But would the opportunity ever arise for me to show him the content of that burden, the beauty of his heritage?

PREPARATIONS FOR TONY'S WEDDING WERE at their peak. I was forced to invent all sorts of activities to justify my frequent absences from the house. I hated the feeling of estrangement and alienation that overcame me — a member of the family with no part in the celebration. I forced myself to behave calmly and to ignore the reproving looks and hurtful remarks. I didn't want to tear myself from my family, but even so the rift grew larger by itself.

Tony hadn't spoken to me since his engagement. He avoided me in general, and didn't even look my way. I knew that he was hurt, and I was afraid that I had lost him forever.

The night before the wedding, my father came into my room. "Amy," he said, in a grave voice, "I hope that you will behave sensibly and come to the wedding." He rested his gaze on me and then continued, "Yes, I know how you feel about the fact that it will be held in a church. But if you decide not to go, you will be causing irreversible damage to our family." I looked down; I couldn't bear his eyes, full of anger, with frustration and pain.

Close to midnight I heard the sound of keys in the metal door of the garage. I quickly turned off the light in my room and walked to the window, trying to catch a glimpse of the precious brother I was losing. By this time tomorrow he and Jean would be on a flight to their new home a thousand miles away. Tony would be starting an internship in an elite hospital, and Jean would be teaching music in a school. I wouldn't be seeing him very often, and not just because of the physical distance. Oh, how far you are from me, my brother! I cried to myself.

As I looked at his profile, illuminated from the garage's dim light, I tried to figure out the expression on his face. Was it happiness? Anxiety? Hope? Suddenly he turned and raised his eyes toward my window; had he felt my gaze? Or perhaps he had thought about our parting, just as I had. Our eyes met in the darkness, I couldn't see beyond the mist of my tears, and I retreated to the darkness of my room. Tony didn't come in. I heard his slow quiet steps on the stairs turn and go away from my room. His door opened and closed and again there was silence.

What would I do tomorrow? I'd had two-and-a-half months to think about whether or not I would participate in the wedding. The number of my flip-flop decisions was the same as the number of days that had passed since then! Even though I had come closer to Judaism, I still had not become acquainted with the concept of "asking a Rav." I didn't know that also in matters of soul-searching one could seek such counsel. I had always been educated to think independently; I had been told time and again that the best decision for me would be the one that I chose by myself. So I chose and chose, and then chose again, and I was more miserable with each decision that I made. "Irreversible damage to our family," my father had said, and I knew that he was right — but was I the one who had caused it?

I took my Shabbos suit out and then returned it to its place. A Shabbos suit in a church? But if I wore everyday clothing it would immediately draw unnecessary attention. Perhaps a new item of clothing? No! New clothing is forbidden to mourners, and I felt like a mourner. In the end I chose a black dress, appropriate for a party, appropriate for a funeral, and appropriate also for the wedding of a Jewish groom in a church...

*   *   *

Closed within myself, I sat in the rented limousine that was taking my family to the wedding. Debbie and Linda sat at my side, looking so pretty in their bridesmaid attire. The whole way they chattered excitedly, and asked me all kinds of upsetting questions; where were they to stand during the ceremony, and were they supposed to kneel in front of the altar? My parents expressed through their calm silence their satisfaction with my "sensible" decision.

The parking area in front of the church was already very full, but we had spaces reserved for us very close to the church gates. Two ushers opened the car doors and escorted my parents with great ceremony to the reception hall. It was lucky that they didn't try to come towards me; I was in such turmoil at that moment I was quite capable even of kicking them! The brightly lit area was full of people. I recognized the mayor of our city, who was a member of our congregation. Rabbi Shneider was there, looking as happy as if he were best man, as well as various Jewish communal leaders; I also saw school administrators and city officials, who had come out of respect for my mother, who had designed their elegant offices. All the Who's Who of our community were there — friends, neighbors, and acquaintances, together with many family members. The latter weighed heavily upon me with their well-wishes, greetings, and kisses, which at that point were about as sweet to my palate as gravel to a parched throat.

The sounds of soft music wafted through the air, and the crowd began to walk towards the hall's interior, a sign that everything was ready.

I walked with the crowd, trying to get swallowed up by it as much as I could. Then I heard a whisper behind me, and I strained to hear, since I heard my name mentioned.

"Why is she so sour?" said voice A.

"Sour? I'd say jealous!" returned voice B.

"Really?"

"Of course!" answered the voice confidently. "Sisters can be very jealous, even to the point of hating the bride."

How little they understood me! I would have given everything I had to be able to be joyous at my dear brother's wedding, if it weren't for the fact that he was abandoning his people and his God on his special day.

I looked at the bride and groom. Tony looked handsome, but a bit too pale; Jean looked like a happy princess. She looked so beautiful, I thought to myself — *and so ugly*, added a voice in my heart. I stood near my family. Rabbi Shneider and the Christian minister stood together, opposite the bride and groom, and the many bridesmaids stood behind. The ceremony began.

My eyes searched the wall for something to fix my gaze on, to take it away from the hurtful scene being enacted in front of me. But even if there had been a thousand distractions I wouldn't have been able to take my gaze away, as it returned of its own accord to the faces of the religious officiators who were trying to unite two different religions with a variety of tactics and the mumbling of empty words.

I heard Tony and Jean answer the Christian minister's questions, I saw Tony put the ring on Jean's finger, and then I heard him repeat after Rabbi Shneider, word for word:

"Thus you are consecrated to me with this ring, in the faith of Moses and Jesus."

I stepped back, ignoring the fact that the crowd's eyes were focused on us. I had to get out of there! I kept on moving backwards until my mother's hand caught me firmly.

"Don't you dare..." she whispered through closed lips.

I stayed there, bound and imprisoned in the rules of this tormenting game.

When the ceremony ended I melted into the crowd, which had begun to walk outside in order to get to the hall where the meal was to be held.

"Amy, congratulations!" I heard a voice next to me. I turned my head and saw my friend Lisa. We fell into each other's arms, and then she studied me. It had been more than two years since we had seen each other.

"You don't look particularly happy," she said finally. I felt free to open my heart to her, and did so without further ado. Lisa was silent.

"I heard from my mother that you're on the road to becoming Orthodox," she said after a pause, "but I didn't imagine that you'd become so extreme."

"It's not a question of extreme," I said. "Tony has cut himself off from our people, and has determined the fate of his children! They'll be Christians, real Christians, do you understand that?"

"Not so much," Lisa admitted. "I don't agree with continuing our people's isolationism in a time when we live exactly like Christians, study with them, and celebrate their holidays. What actually differentiates us from them? History? A hostile past? I think that it can all be bridged over with a little love," she said with a smile.

"Oh, Lisa, no one here can understand me, even *you*! Our education has been so distorted, we don't even feel the lack of our national identity. That's exactly what Tony found so hard to understand. What really differentiates us from them? For me Jewish identity is an eternal possession which must never be given up, and certainly not thrown away with such ease."

Lisa was silent for a moment and then said, "Tell me, how is it that you got to where you are now, if the education that we had leads us in the opposite direction?"

I was surprised by the question. "I don't know," I answered thoughtfully, "but I was always hungry for more Judaism. Finding Jewish content fascinated me, and I always searched for more. From that search I got to know many meaningful things that had been missing in my life, and I hope to fill that void with the rich heritage of our people."

"I wish you success on your path," said Lisa, "and I hope that you'll be a good friend and wish me success on my path."

"If I love you sincerely, Lisa, then I have to hope that you *don't* succeed in your path, so that you'll find your way to the truth. There's no symmetry or balance here. If your values and mine were from the same human source, then you would be correct in your request for balance. But because one source is Divine and the other is human, I can't wish you success as you want me to."

Lisa took my hand. "Come, Amy, let's forget about this for the time being," she said. "Here we are together — let's enjoy our friendship after such a long separation."

I took the hint, and stopped talking about what really obsessed me. Lisa's cheerfulness and genuine friendship eased my gloom somewhat, but even so I had no success at all at taking part in the occasion.

 DURING MY LAST YEAR IN COLLEGE, I RECEIVED an invitation to an important meeting with Rabbi Shneider. When I got there I saw that I wasn't the only one invited to this meeting. Also attending were Herbert Poll, chairman of the United Hebrew Congregations; John Tanner, one of Rabbi Shneider's senior advisors; Laura Smith, the feminist chairperson of the Reform community; Dan Hertzberg, educational administrator of the Reform Agnon day school in our town; Shilat Mann, a representative of the Israelis in the community; Daniella Golomov, "our woman" in the Jewish Agency; Mona Richman, chairperson of our local sport organization for Jewish youth, as well as many others from Reform community organizations in our area. Herbert Poll opened the meeting by heaping praise on Rabbi Shneider, who had reaped so many impressive achievements in our community as well as in the United Hebrew Congregations in all of America.

"As Rabbi Shneider is one of the more active promoters of the subject of this meeting tonight," said Poll, "I will honor him by letting him make his presentation first."

Rabbi Shneider explained the background to the meeting, emphasizing that he was introducing a program in its beginning stages.

"The United Hebrew Congregations has decided," Rabbi

Shneider announced, "that the time has come to expand the area of Reform influence to Jewish centers outside of the United States. The first target country is Israel. As everyone here knows, the difference in mentality between a Jew in America and a Jew in Israel is so great that it demands a new and well-thought out preparedness."

Shilat Mann nodded her head energetically, in agreement with every word.

"Allow me to include you in the internal discussions that we had in the Union regarding our chances of success in Israel. We researched the subject thoroughly, assisted, of course, by our representatives who had been sent to Israel to feel the political and social "pulse" there. We also got help from those Israelis who are members of our community. We came to the conclusion that we have the capability of influencing two strata of Israeli society: the elite, meaning various political and media leaders, and the youth.

"The middle-aged population won't be so interested in our messages, whether because they lack faith and any interest at all in Judaism, or because they are too traditional and would recoil from us.

"Our program, therefore, is twofold. We will inject considerable amounts of money into the leadership and their candidates so that they can advance their own agendas, and we will conduct for them, at our expense of course, exciting trips to the United States. There we will introduce them to our congregations, and let them see the scope of our activities our community programs, our schools, in short, let them see what our strength is. In return they will be obligated to represent our interests in all matters of religious legislation.

"The second track is more sensitive, and with it we want to bring the youth close, the secular youth who are so cut off from all Jewish experience and values. We want to pursue this track also with camps and trips throughout the United States. Their youth are interested in exploring the world, something that is the dream of every average Israeli, and if we are smart and give them that with full subsidies, they will be more inclined to lend an ear to our ideas, and maybe even join us.

"We have another common interest with the Israeli leadership as well as with the youth — to weaken the influence of the ultra-Orthodox, the *chareidim*, which is spreading throughout Israel in a demographic as well as an ideological manner. In this, together with our parallel Israeli staff, we are investing most of our skills and financial resources. We want to mold Israeli public opinion and show them that Reform Judaism will bring pluralism to Israel and lessen the coercive influence of the ultra-Orthodox.

"All of you sitting here serve in important organizational positions in our community. Therefore, there are none better than you to offer advice on these two tracks of influence that we've chosen. We must understand that the success of our campaign in Israel will be determined by our hard work, in terms of both the time and the thought that we put into the matter. Each of you sitting here must contribute his share towards the success of the project. If every Reform congregation in the major cities in the United States will do the same, we will succeed in 'conquering' the State of Israel! Therefore, I would like you to divide into two work groups: each will prepare a detailed plan for one of the tracks we've discussed."

There was silence. Someone asked why Israel was chosen as the first goal, and why we weren't first expanding our area of influence somewhere where we were wanted and known.

Rabbi Shneider answered that Israel had been chosen for two reasons: (1) If the Jewish State were to recognize Reform as a legitimate branch of Judaism, it would be the biggest achievement for the movement since its inception, because there is no authoritative Jewish body greater than the State of Israel; and, (2) The population in Israel is constantly changing. Many non-Jews live there today and their numbers will grow. They will surely need Reform's "vital services," such as its conversions, in order to live as Jews in Israel.

Another few questions were asked and then we divided into two work groups. I, of course, was expected to join the group that was to deal with the youth. I was troubled by Rabbi Shneider's speech, and his stated intentions were leading me to a confrontation with my conscience.

A date was set for the next meeting and everyone parted with handshakes. The main "patroness," Shilat Mann, took advantage of the last moments to emphasize her acquaintance with Israeli youth and how important it was to influence them with the proposed trips and sports camps and other such things.

"I myself arrived here as a teenager on a trip organized by the Jewish Agency and the Reform community," she said with pride, "and ever since then I have been an active member."

I wandered around the Temple waiting for the chance to speak with Rabbi Shneider directly. In my opinion the meeting had left more than just a little bad taste.

Rabbi Shneider invited me to sit down. "I see that you want to speak with me, Amy. And the fact is, this is an opportunity to find out how you are, how your studies are going, and what your plans are for next year."

"Rabbi Shneider," I began, straight and to the point, ignoring his warm greeting, which was bound to make it hard for me to say what I wanted to say to him. "Rabbi Shneider, it seems to me that the aims of tonight's meeting are, well, sort of missionary..."

Rabbi Shneider chuckled. "You're always so extreme in your definitions, Amy! I would call them *educational* aims."

"No, it's different!" I said. "You spoke very clearly about all sorts of methods like trips and recreational activities, to make Israeli youth affiliate themselves with Reform. That's not education. That's enticement!"

"I don't look at it that way, Amy," said Rabbi Shneider. "Surely you remember your own impressions from your trip to Israel — you told me then that Israeli youth were devoid of Jewish values — isn't that right? So we can introduce them to those values. What's wrong with that?"

"It's a question of what method you use," I said. "In matters of belief and opinion it's not right to use methods of enticement. Every person should choose his own belief and values with real deliberation."

"Amy," Rabbi Shneider's voice was authoritative, "can it be that you're so naïve? Don't you understand that the main point of *your* position in our congregation's youth group served the same aims and with the same means that are so 'flawed' in your eyes?"

I was filled with consternation for a moment, but I gathered up my courage and replied, "Rabbi Shneider, I'm not naïve. When the community pumped in so much funding for our activities, I immediately understood that it was serving various interests. But then it involved youth that anyway belonged to our congregation, which is not the same as an attempt to make outsiders belong."

"I just want them to taste Jewish values and our way of life," said Rabbi Shneider smoothly.

"If that's your intention, Rabbi Shneider, then why don't you invite them for group discussions and lectures given by thinking people? That way they'll confront the issues openly and honestly."

"Amy," said Rabbi Shneider, "don't you think recreation and enjoyment are a more pleasant way?"

"Possibly, but it's not honest," I replied.

"Honest?" Rabbi Shneider paused. "Let's reach our goal, and then we can talk about 'honest'."

"And what would God think about such a statement?"

"Ahh..." Rabbi Shneider smiled. "But I have a question that comes one step before yours. Before we worry about what God's opinion might be, should we not first ask whether He exists at all?"

I hadn't expected that! I stared at him, speechless. "You can't mean...Rabbi Shneider...that you don't believe that God exists?!"

"I didn't say that — you did," he replied calmly.

"But...you're a *rabbi*! And what about all your sermons and everything..."

"The matter is very simple, my dear. I provide my congregants with what they ask for. Human beings in general, and especially Jews in particular, want to believe that there is a Power above them that guides the world. Every person, within his deepest self, wants to know that there exists a loving Father who is taking care of everything. I, as a Rabbi, help them to fill that need."

"And you don't believe it yourself?" I whispered, shaken.

"Let's say, my dear, that my approach to Judaism — its ethical value system and its long tradition — doesn't depend upon whether or not God exists."

"But that's awful!" I cried. "To tell people things because that's what they want to hear?"

"It's not so terrible. Take a lawyer, for instance, who knows that his client broke the law. He 'sells' legal lies to the court in order to prove that his client is innocent."

"What's a 'legal lie'?"

"Taking advantage of all the loopholes in the law, skillful use of argumentation, playing with what will influence the jury — in short, whatever a lawyer does in order to prove his client innocent. Why are you so upset? I 'sell' people something that I don't necessarily believe, to give them a good feeling. And the lawyer 'sells' things to the court, that he doesn't believe, for monetary gain."

Again I was speechless. I knew Rabbi Shneider well — he didn't choose the example of a lawyer at random. He knew full well what my academic plans were, and he was hinting that I would be no better than he.

But I didn't give in. "Rabbi Shneider, I find it difficult to accept the parallel that you make between a lawyer and a rabbi, because Jewish ethics aren't something you 'sell' to clients. It could be that a professional provides merchandise within the boundaries that the law establishes and permits, and it could be that because those boundaries are human they are not always correct or just. But Jewish ethics are from God, and are just and true by definition. I think a rabbi is *more* obligated to believe when he is trying to lead his flock than another professional is in the area of his expertise."

"I don't accept your argument," said Rabbi Shneider authoritatively. "I don't see any difference between a rabbi and another professional. A lawyer specializes in preparing lawsuits, and I specialize in matters of ethics and religion. Both of us sell a service to our clients according to their requirements!"

"If that's so, Rabbi Shneider," I said, terribly distraught, "then...I guess I have to tell you that I can't continue to be your 'client.' I find it difficult to absorb what I've heard from you this evening."

"That is to say..." Rabbi Shneider made an attempt to soften the effect of my words with a smile.

"That is to say...," I said, "I'm resigning, both from my position as chairman of the youth group and as a member of your congregation." I rose and turned towards the door.

"Slow down, Amy," he said. "Don't think I don't know that everything you've said to me tonight stems from your infatuation with the Orthodox. And I know you well enough to know that you'll try to create a new way of life for yourself because of this. But listen well to what I'm telling you, Amy: *They'll reject you.* And I'll tell you also, that despite all the insolence you've shown me tonight, we will take you back with open arms, without trying to settle accounts. Mark my words — you'll find them useful one day."

I couldn't look at him. I just got up and left the room, the Temple, Rabbi Shneider, and his path.

The hot summer night's air greeted my burning face as I closed the heavy oak doors of the Temple behind me. This was a night full of destiny for me. A night in which I had left a central part of my life — my role, my position, and the leader I had held in such high esteem. Actually, though, since I had drawn nearer to Orthodoxy, his image had begun to lose some of its former status for me. I could see that there were a lot of problems in the ideas he tried to impart to us, his flock. Now, however, I had made a final break and I felt the pain of one who has wavered between two paths for too long, and is finally forced to choose one and leave the other behind.

Perhaps I had lacked courage, or perhaps in my innocence I had thought that I could continue to be active in the Reform congregation despite the changes in my outlook and practice. Now, though, on this night, the truth had hit me harshly in the face.

It isn't easy for a person to see the weakness of his spiritual mentor revealed. And to discover that such a figure denies the very existence of God! For me, Rabbi Shneider had stood for American Judaism, the moderate intelligentsia, culture at its best, and great leadership. Despite the changes that had taken place in me I still had nothing to take his place! I had nothing to go to, from that which I had just abandoned.

I stood in pain, next to my car, alone in my new path, already paying the price for trying to acquaint myself with my roots and my heritage.

As I drove up to our house, I rolled down the window and heard the soft sounds of a guitar spilled out into the driveway. It was Linda, who played so well. I parked the car and sat listening to the music, trying to put off taking the last steps towards the house. The guitar soothed my pain without my knowing it. I leaned my head on the steering wheel and let the tears flow, to wash the cracked earth of my spirit, to wash and soften it; perhaps afterwards it would come to be plowed anew.

I don't know how long I sat there, until suddenly I felt a soft tap on my shoulder. It was my father, who had just come home from work and found me as I was. I raised my moist eyes to him; he was surprised, but didn't ask any questions.

"It isn't easy to change course in life," I said, wanting to explain.

"Definitely not," he said. "But if the new course is so painful, wouldn't it be better to take a more comfortable path?"

"But the new path is the *right* one, and it makes me happier, Dad."

"You don't look so happy to me! And is that why you're crying?" He smiled.

"No, I *am* happy! And yes, I'm crying because it's so hard to leave the path that was mine for my whole life."

"Amy," my father sighed, "to tell you the truth, I find it difficult to understand what's come over you. If your new path is causing you so much pain, is it worthwhile?"

"Clearly! But every loss causes pain, Dad, even necessary ones."

My father looked at me. "And I," he said, "I long for the Amy that I lost."

"And I long for my roots. And yours," I added.

"Well, then," said my father, "I suggest we long together, in the house! Let's go in!"

WE SAT, TWO HUNDRED AND THIRTY STUDENTS, in one of the spacious halls of the State University. We had all registered to study law. All of us had at least one university degree, and all had excelled in one way or another. Out of 2,000 students who had taken the grueling LSAT examinations, only we had been accepted. All of us were ambitious; the law school was among the most prestigious in the United States, and demanded an especially high level of achievement.

We sat quietly as the dean of the university welcomed us with friendly greetings. After a few opening words he came to the point:

"Ladies and gentlemen, look to your right, look to the fellow student at your left — together you are three. For every three of you who are sitting here today, only two will be left at our school at the end of the next semester! And at the end of the following semester, perhaps even less. Our Law School opens its gates to you, but know that in order to remain within its gates, a 'war of survival' awaits you. Prepare yourselves for the struggle. Invest all your energy in your studies. He who studies survives, and he who survives wins. Welcome!"

This terrifying opening definitively cast us into the deep and demanding waters of the law school. "He who studies survives, and he who survives wins!" was a slogan internalized by all; and everyone wanted to survive.

The competition was unbelievable. During the first semester we took five courses, and for each one we had to attain complete mastery over thick volumes on law theory. In general the lectures were riveting, but our teachers set nearly unreachable standards. We diligently summarized their classes in our notebooks, for good summaries were the key to success. However, because each of us knew that the survival of his fellow classmate would affect his own survival, almost no social ties were formed — to the point where, if someone missed a day or two, he knew that no one would lend him his notebook to make up lost material or even to look at, and in the first months no one even tried.

By the time the semester came to an end, the tension was palpable. Therefore I was alarmed when I realized that I was coming down with something. My fever rose, I had a cough, my throat hurt, and I was shivering uncontrollably. Still I sat in the lecture hall, wondering what I would do the next day. When I realized that I wouldn't be able to last till the end of the class, I left the hall slowly, and with great difficulty drove home.

As I entered the house, my mother looked at me with dismay.

"It's nothing," I said, "just a bit of flu." Dr. Kagan arrived an hour later, and made the following diagnosis: "You've got severe tonsillitis, young lady, on top of a bad case of the flu," he said. "I'm prescribing antibiotics and at least one week of bed rest." With that news, I began to shiver even more under the covers! A week! To stay away from my studies for a week could mean the end of all my academic plans. Many lecturers summarized their material in enormous detail; others crammed us with examples from various law cases. And this final material always appeared in the tests, the veteran students warned us. But there was nothing to be done.

The days passed by slowly, and as soon as my fever was gone, I got up, dressed in especially warm clothing, as I was still subject to attacks of shivering, and headed for the door.

"What are you doing?" asked my mother in alarm.

"I'm going to university," I answered. "I've already missed enough material, and I'm afraid I may have lost my opportunity to study law altogether."

"A week makes such a difference?" she asked.

"Yes. The summaries at the end of the course are vital, and there are lecturers who place difficulties in the tests with the clear intention that we should fail. And you know, the prestige of the place depends on how difficult it is to survive in it!"

"Awful!" said my mother, summarizing my opinion as well.

Once I got to class, I was still too weak to concentrate. I looked around for someone, anyone, whom I could ask just to leaf through his notebook, in his presence. But no one had noticed me or even felt my absence, I thought bitterly.

I looked from one to the other, wondering. "Without a doubt, he wouldn't let me... her? Certainly not! I've never met anyone so competitive... him? It's questionable whether he even understands the material," and so on.

Suddenly I saw her — how had I not thought of her? Almost certainly she would lend me her notebook. I didn't know her name, but I knew her. She wore her hair in a short braid and she stood out with her modest dress, even more than I did. She always stayed in the background, and I had almost never even heard her voice. A quick glance at her face revealed intelligent eyes, and her facial expression was refined; a lone, yet elegant wolf, I told myself. I decided to try.

"Hello," I said. "I'm Amy."

"Pleased to meet you. I'm Rachel," she said with a smile. We shook hands.

"You haven't been here for a few days."

"That's right," I said with surprise. "You noticed?"

"Of course," she laughed. "There was no one to ask my questions out loud!"

We both laughed. "Is that why you're so quiet in class?" I asked with a smile.

"Sure — there's someone to do the work for me. By the way, if you need to see notes to make up the material you missed," she said, again gracefully, "I can lend you mine until tomorrow. You can photocopy it if you want."

"Rachel," I said emotionally, "until now I didn't know that I've been asking your questions. But now you've succeeded in answering all of *mine*!"

Her notebook reinforced my impression of her. She was exemplary in her neatness and exactness. Her summaries were concise and clear, and she was obviously also talented in taking notes quickly, judging by the many source references she had succeeded in noting down. Even more, though, I valued her willingness to lend me her notebook — a social anomaly in our guild!

It was only natural that a friendship develop between us after that. I began to appreciate Rachel even more when she told me that she had attended a Bais Yaakov and came from an Orthodox home. She told me that her father had been brought up in the path of "Torah with *derech eretz*" by his father, who himself had been a student of that original path in Germany. Because of that he believed that his children should study in Bais Yaakov and yeshiva until they were 19, and then to study an academic profession that would support them with dignity.

"I'm the oldest," said Rachel, "and it was very difficult for me to get used to the transition from Bais Yaakov Seminary to the university. I've been very lonely here, but for obvious reasons I have to guard my privacy. I'm lucky to have another woman like me here — you," she said.

She was surprised to discover that I came from a Reform home and that I'd begun to come closer to Judaism on my own.

"You've probably run into quite a few difficulties," she said with respect. "And how do you manage on Shabbos?"

I told her that I bought my food at a kosher restaurant and that I spent every Shabbos by myself in my house.

"Really? All alone? And what about shul?"

"I haven't gone to an Orthodox synagogue," I said. "There isn't one in walking distance from my house, and anyway, I don't know if I'm ready to...to enter the Orthodox experience."

She looked at me thoughtfully. "And holidays?"

"I stay in the house on holidays too."

"I'd love to have you over for Shabbos and the holidays!" Rachel said with great sincerity. "My parents are punctilious about having guests every Shabbos and holiday. We'd all be very happy if you'd be our guest."

I assented to her request hesitantly, unsure of what it would be like.

Rachel's house gradually became my Shabbos and holiday residence. I spent wonderful Sabbaths there, exactly what I had longed for. Sabbaths filled with peace of mind and inner joy, with studying Torah and uplifting of the spirit. I became part of a family Shabbos table, singing *zemiros* and hearing *divrei Torah*. Rachel's family took me in with open arms every time anew. They were sensitive and wise enough to make me feel like one of the family.

*   *   *

Because I didn't want to become completely dependent on Rachel's family, I stayed home every other Shabbos. The situation at home, though, had become unbearable. The fact that I ordered prepared Shabbos meals angered my mother. "They probably prepared that food two weeks ago," she'd say.

The smell of the cholent and the way it looked made her nauseous. I would sit at the table with everyone, but everything that I ate and did differentiated me very clearly from them.

My parents had treated me with great tolerance as long as they thought my Shabbos observance was only a passing phase, but when I began to spend every other Shabbos at Rachel's they understood how serious I was and that disturbed them very much. The atmosphere at home became more troubled with each passing week, until I decided — enough!

"I've rented the Goldbergs' little basement apartment," I announced to my parents one evening as we sat in the living room drinking coffee.

"Are you opening your own law studio?" asked my father in jest.

"Not exactly," I said, trying to keep my tone light. "Maybe a Shabbos studio." That was a mistake on my part.

The smile froze on his face and he put down his coffee cup on the table. "What do you mean?" he asked sharply.

"I...I feel that I'm overburdening the family with my Shabbos, um, table," I stammered. "And I thought it would be better if I had my own...well, corner, every Shabbos, where I could observe Shabbos as I like, without spoiling the peace in our house."

My mother looked at me with restrained fury. "After everything we've done for you, it's still not enough? I stopped serving meat meals, we bought you a separate set of dishes and a Shabbos hotplate, and every Shabbos you have food that smells awful. You wander around like a homeless beggar in other people's houses — and now you want to make Shabbos in the Goldbergs' basement? You can't find a corner for yourself in our ten-room house?"

"Sue," my father turned to my mother, "Sue, don't get so upset. I don't think there's any logic in it, but if that's what Amy wants we'll let her do it until she comes to her senses."

"Comes to her senses? I don't think that will ever happen. Something went wrong four years ago, and it has just been getting worse. She's sinking deeper and deeper into this fundamentalist mud!"

My father was silent.

I sat shrunken in the armchair. I had hurt and angered my mother and upset my father. I felt terrible.

"Go ahead!" my mother said bitterly. "If our spacious home is too small to contain all your crazy ideas, go and spend your Shabbos in someone's dark and miserable basement, and feel more comfortable!"

*   *   *

The Goldbergs' basement was indeed dark, but it was comfortable. From the windows I had a view of feet walking in the street, and a little bit of light made its way through. But there was a separate entrance and adjacent parking, so I really could not ask for more than that.

On Friday afternoon I loaded all my Shabbos needs into the car, trying to do it so that none of my family members would notice, something that was nearly impossible. I took cleaning materials, bedding, a night-light, some clothing, the Shabbos hotplate, a tablecloth, and food that I'd bought. I wished everyone a good Shabbos but no one answered me, and I left.

I arrived at my "Shabbos home" and within a short time I had scrubbed the two basement rooms until they sparkled. I set the small kitchen table and dragged it into the "living room," that was completely empty. I'll have to furnish this place to feel more at home here, I thought to myself. By the time I'd finished all my other Shabbos preparations I could see through the windows that the sun had already begun to set. I could see feet treading on a sidewalk bathed in pink light. I studied the calendar that Rachel had bought for me, and discovered that I had half an hour until candle-lighting. I sat down on the chair and, even though I would have preferred a comfortable couch, let myself rest. I took a deep breath and looked around. It was a basement, but Shabbos was coming and it felt like it.

Suddenly I heard several knocks on the door.

Who could it be?

I opened the door and cried out in surprise— in the doorway stood my sisters Debbie and Linda, smiling and holding packages in their hands. "Mom and Dad are also coming!" they whispered happily.

"Come in, come in," I said, completely mixed up, but overjoyed.

My parents then appeared. "We've come to spend Shabbos with you," Dad announced cheerfully. "Where's the Shabbos hotplate?" I pointed to its place in the kitchenette. I was speechless.

"We've brought our meals," said my father. "We bought everything at your kosher restaurant. Don't ask how quickly we drove there in order to buy this before they closed!"

It was unbelievable!

Debbie and Linda went up and down the stairs bringing in the folding chairs and disposable utensils, while my mother quickly set the small table. Everything was ready.

I lit the Shabbos candles, and all of a sudden my mother approached. Near my two candles she placed two silver candlesticks of her own and placed candles in them. She lit them and covered her eyes. I don't know what she prayed for at that emotional moment but *I* prayed that all our Friday nights be like this one.

"Whose idea was this?" I whispered to Debbie when my mother was conducting a get-acquainted tour of the second room.

"Mom's," she whispered back.

"Really?" I had been sure that my father had suggested it.

"When you left the house this afternoon," Debbie told me quickly, "she cried a lot, and said, 'Why can't I get along with my oldest daughter?' Dad said that it probably was because they didn't have enough patience. Afterwards they talked so quietly that I didn't hear anything, and Mom told Dad he had to hurry to buy food and Mom gave us lots of orders, and then we came!"

"So dark!" My mother expressed her opinion about "my" basement. "And it's furnished like a Dominican monk's room — but at least it's clean."

We sat on the simple chairs, talked a bit, and afterwards I said the Friday night prayers. They waited patiently until I had finished. Then my father stood and made Kiddush, and all of us enjoyed the kosher food — even my mother, who said, "It's not so bad!" I took it as a compliment.

My father remembered a melody from some distant Shabbos *zemiros* and sang it for me several times. The atmosphere was pleasant and warm, and again we felt like a happy and united family.

"It was nice," said my father at the end, "but I would have preferred that you stay with us."

I shook my head wordlessly. It was almost midnight when I accompanied them out. "I'm going to sleep here tonight," I told my mother, who, I knew, was hoping I'd come back with them. "All my things are here, so...I can't take them from here to the house because according to Halachah it's forbidden to carry things without an *eiruv*."

"What are you talking about?" said my mother. "Put your things in the car and we'll take them home for you, and you can walk if you want to."

I sighed. No matter what I did or didn't say, it was difficult. "I'll stay here," I said gently. "But I'll come tomorrow."

"What do you mean? We're coming to *you* tomorrow! All our food is on your hotplate."

"Sorry," I mumbled. "Of course, you're coming tomorrow." My mother nodded, trying hard to be understanding. "Good night, good night," they called to me as they got into the car. "*Gut Shabbos*," I replied, and hurried to go back into my little Shabbos world before the sound of the engine would rip apart the holiness of the night.

It was very nice of them, whispered an inner voice. *But*

how long will they be able to keep it up? asked a second voice. *What difference does it make? They came toward you, and now you have to do the same for them. You might have to compromise on a few things.*

The first voice was adamant. *Only Reform Jews do that!*

What difference does it make? argued the second voice. *Honor your father and your mother — that's also written in the Torah.*

Yes, but not at the expense of the sanctity of Shabbos.

Who determines what's permitted and what's not?

God does! Not your intellect. If you don't understand that yet, then you're still Reform.

So God doesn't want me to honor my parents?

Who said that? Honor them, but when it comes to Halachah tell them nicely what is and isn't permissible.

I tried and failed.

Try again, but think well beforehand... you have to make an effort in order to succeed, as in everything.

The voices within me said all the familiar painful things. I push forward and pull back. How long could I go on like this?

*   *   *

The next Shabbos, as I walked in the park with Rachel, we looked for a quiet corner so that we could talk away from the crowds. I told her about the previous Shabbos. "Every step that I make toward Jewish observance distances me from my parents. Then I feel that I have to go more slowly, in order to move away from them less. You know, in the four years since I began to move closer to Jewish observance, I've succeeded in keeping kosher and in observing Shabbos, but there is *so much* I don't know!"

Rachel listened to me intently, and then said to me in her gentle voice, "You know, we have many *ba'alei teshuvah* as guests, and if I compare the process that you're going through to that which most of them go through, I can see certain differences."

"What do you mean?"

Rachel chose her words carefully, and I understood from her explanation that most *ba'alei teshuvah* tried to fulfill each new mitzvah that they encountered, to the maximum. The tendency, she explained, was to take upon themselves strict adherence to the law plus added embellishments, so much so that the rabbis often had to cool down their extreme enthusiasm to make sure that they didn't collapse under the heavy burden they tried to load upon themselves! But with me, Rachel pointed out, it seemed to be the opposite: with every new mitzvah that I encountered, I seemed to always look for the minimum observance of it, the compromise, what I could do without having to change too much.

I thought about her words for a moment, and then replied, both to Rachel and to myself, "Yes, you're right. That's exactly how it is with me. Maybe you can explain to me what causes my 'minimalist' attitude?"

Rachel was uncomfortable with the question. She was quiet for a few minutes. "It seems to me," she began, that the difference between you and many *ba'alei teshuvah* lies in your backgrounds. That is, the *ba'alei teshuvah* that I know usually come from a completely assimilated milieu, one that has no connection to or knowledge of Judaism. Therefore their first encounter with it leaves them stunned. They examine the matter intellectually, "discover the truth," and then they storm all the mitzvos with enthusiasm!

"But *you*," she went on, "have a strong Jewish background — albeit a familiarity with a different Judaism. The observant way of life is what appealed to you, *not* simply the knowledge that Judaism is Divine truth! You take it in small portions because you see it as something which enriches your own inner life, but not beyond that."

"Yes," I nodded, surprised by her line of thought. "You're right. I wasn't so much searching for truth — what I was familiar with was — almost — good enough for me. But I just wanted *more* of it. More of it felt more authentic, somehow. I think," I went on, "that this is the first time that I've understood that my Reform background hasn't really brought me closer to Judaism. In a way you might say that it's dampened my enthusiasm!"

Rachel remained silent.

"It's funny, I'd always thought the opposite," I said thoughtfully. We began to walk around the lovely lake, while continuing to talk. We passed the many places where I'd had such good times with my family on so many Saturday afternoon outings. The thought flashed through my mind that they might actually be there now — and I found myself wondering who my father was playing tennis with.

Yes, I sighed, she's right, I'm used to thinking that compromises are good, that Reform has an advantage over the Jewish secularism that doesn't recognize Judaism at all. It was suddenly clear to me that my tolerant Reform approach was in fact restraining me from the enthusiasm and devotion necessary to change and be changed.

"What should I do?"

"Maybe it would good for you to study, go to classes in Judaism, and not just experience keeping the mitzvos," replied Rachel. "Maybe it would help if you began to understand the world of Judaism from the starting point that the Torah comes from God. Maybe then you'll have the strength to make the changes in your life that you want, but haven't yet entirely succeeded in achieving."

After Shabbos, Rachel gave me the name of Rabbi Yehudah Pell and the address and phone number where he taught classes for women. We parted in friendship. This time I was equipped with a signpost in my hand to mark the way — so that I wouldn't draw back or stumble.

IN RAV PELL'S CLASSES I BEGAN TO BECOME acquainted with the fascinating face of Judaism. With the Torah — a Torah of truth; with the prophets — prophets of truth; with their prophecies, which were and will be realized. I learned that they weren't just moral tales or parables, as I had been taught. I learned about the Torah's chain of transmission and of observance, the Written Torah and its secrets, the Oral Torah and its ties to the written Torah.

Rav Pell spoke of science and Torah and the reasons for the mitzvos. All of this was new to me — amazing, wonderful. Despite my heavy load of studies at the university, I attended his classes at least one day a week.

The superficiality and paucity of my acquaintance with Jewish concepts began to disappear, and in its stead came depth of thought. I learned that Judaism wasn't just a pleasant and satisfying way of life, among many others; it was first and foremost a message from God to man, without which man's world is one of intellectual and moral chaos.

Yes, Rachel was right. The classes' influence on me also expressed itself in the way I kept the mitzvos. I began to understand the value of the *"pachim ketanim,"* the little things, and was more careful in keeping them.

Finally I was moving forward with both feet! I also received good advice from the Rav about confrontations with my parents, and with his wise guidance I began to explain less and to express my respect and esteem for them more, by my actions. The atmosphere in the house became more tolerable, but the confrontations didn't stop altogether.

Our law studies were progressing at the same time, and Rachel and I studied diligently day and night; we had decided that we would pass the fateful hurdles with a high mark that would assure our futures, both in the university and in the profession. The tests were difficult, too difficult, but thank God we passed them successfully.

In the second semester, we were able to choose what courses we wanted to take. We chose: preparing agreements, law theory, criminal law, and appearing in court.

Professor Albright was the lecturer of the first course. He was an outstanding lecturer with great personal charm. Every class with him was an exceptional experience.

Professor Hertz, on the other hand, was very strict. His lectures were packed with details upon details, and he demanded that we have good command of them. His tests were difficult and at times even impossible. Towards the end of the second semester and its final examinations, everyone feared Professor Hertz's.

His test consisted of an assignment to write wills according to figures that were given to us. It was so difficult that sixty percent of the students failed. The student body submitted a complaint to the university administration that a considerable portion of the test material had not been studied. The complaint was rejected.

The next day Professor Hertz came into the lecture hall, surveyed us all with his piercing eyes, and then said with a satisfied smile, "You failed? So you failed!"

Our numbers were fewer at the end of the second semester, but we knew that whoever had survived the first two semesters would remain until the end.

Rachel and I found our marks on the bulletin board. The scale of grades was between 4 and 0; but no student had ever received 4. My final mark was 3.72, and hers was 3.75; these were the best marks. Whoever came close to 4 was considered outstanding, and whoever got less than 2 was simply not considered at all! The intermediate students ranged between 2 and 3. Those with the ten highest marks became assistant lecturers and their future was assured.

The struggle had essentially ended. The fierce competition was over, the academic tension decreased, and the students turned their attention to forming friendships among themselves. The atmosphere became pleasant, and in general these were the happiest days of a law student's education. Various firms set up interviews with the outstanding students and accepted them for part-time positions while they were still studying. Students whose final marks were below 3 were not invited for interviews.

Rachel received two work offers with important firms, but she refused them.

"I don't feel that I'd be able to fit into these places, because of the atmosphere there," she said with a smile. "I assured my father that I would work at a place that's suitable for an Orthodox Jewish woman."

I waited impatiently for job proposals and I received one that was excellent. The firm of Kreitzer and Fishbein signed a contract with me for a year's work. The salary was very good for a student who had just finished the first year. Now I would have to invest great effort to keep up with my classes in Judaism and my university studies as well.

Kreitzer and Fishbein took in three top students every year. Their offices took up a five-story building in the center of town. Many lawyers worked in the huge spaces that were divided by decorative partitions to make up "open rooms." The partitions were numbered, and there was a hierarchy also in the building's floors. The first and second stories belonged to the elite staff, and they were the lawyers who generally appeared in court. On the third floor were the huge library, a legal archive, and a wide lobby for those perusing. The fourth and fifth floors comprised the staffs of the junior lawyers and interns. They were the ones who did all the menial tasks, like clarifying legal precedents.

The legal work at Kreitzer and Fishbein was done in teams, each one headed by a senior lawyer who gave guidelines and edited the final material. Advancement of everyone in the office depended to a large extent on the team heads, based on the recommendations that he gave and also on the quality of the work presented to him. There were many secretaries, who incessantly typed legal material and also did standard secretarial work. Kreitzer and Fishbein themselves oversaw it all; they were clever veteran lawyers who had spread their fear over many a defendant, not to mention those working in their large and successful firm.

My parents were very proud that I had a job in such a respected office; at least in the academic sphere I hadn't disappointed them.

Only students who hadn't yet been accepted to workplaces invested time in their studies during the third year. The rest belittled it, and came in just for the sake of appearance, or to share experiences in different legal matters in a forum of intelligent and learned students. There were simulated trials towards the end of the second semester, and they were a first-class legal and social experience. Top lawyers and representatives from their firms sat in the audience to judge the talents of the new lawyers and to select from the best of them. We related to the trials more as an experience than as a test.

The high point of these mock trials was when we were given a quarter of an hour to put together a team to represent one of the sides in a trial without being told whether it would be the prosecution or the defense. A quarter of an hour later we had to present our argument before the audience. With great seriousness we presented improvised arguments, while each of us tried to cover the gaps that the other had left in his arguments. More than once, laughter threatened to burst out, but on the outside we were frighteningly somber and tough.

The last real hurdle was the end-of-the-year tests, but unlike the semester tests, these could be taken again until the student received a passing grade. At our law school there was never a second time around to take a semester test, and a student who failed was not given an opportunity to make good his loss.

 RACHEL RECEIVED A POSITION WITH AN Orthodox firm at the beginning of the year. Because of our schedules, we didn't always meet at the university, so most of our meetings were in her house. During the High Holidays, I spent most of the time with her family.

*   *   *

The setting sun painted the sky red, and a pink mist filled the air. As I gazed, it seemed to melt into the horizon, and something inside me seemed to melt as well. The Days of Awe were coming to their peak, overtaking the heart with fear and trembling.

The final preparations for Yom Kippur were taking place in Rachel's house, quietly and seriously. It was different from the bustling activity of Friday afternoon, before Shabbos. Even the small children contained their merriment. Their boisterous eyes twinkled, but the atmosphere affected them also.

As Rachel's father wrapped himself in his *tallis*, his graying beard trembled and his eyes were closed in concentration, his face tense: the last few moments before Yom Kippur.

Rachel's mother stood near the candles, dressed all in white. Her face was noble and serene as her nine children entered the room to receive their parents' blessings before the holiest day of the year.

The first son, Yitzchak, steps towards his father, his face reflecting the awe of the moment; he bends his head as his father's hands envelop him with affection. I hear the ancient words of the parental blessing from his father's trembling lips, entreating and pleading. His mother's eyes are filled with tears, utter silence in the room surrounds the holy words with which Jewish fathers have blessed their children throughout the generations, penetrating silently into the depths of the soul.

The father has finished and Yitzchak lifts his head, kisses his father and turns towards his mother to receive her blessing also. She blesses him quietly, and her voice is not heard, but waves of warmth and love hover in the air as the blessing binds parents with children, in the prayer that comes forth from the depths at this precious moment, this holy moment. Rachel, who has already received her blessing, stands by me. Shlomo, Na'amah, and all the other children pass before me like a moving film, with the beautiful timeless faces of Jewish children. They will enter the gate of Yom Kippur clothed in blessings and love.

Tears fill my eyes and course silently down my cheeks, tears that purify me from other preparations for this day that I had known in previous years, preparations that were so different, preparations that seem to desecrate the soft trembling I feel within myself now.

Lake Drive is filling with people, each greeting the other with a flutter of the eyelash. Not a sound is heard, and only the echo of steps in cloth shoes fills the space. They walk slowly and simply, as Jews have always done on *erev Yom Kippur*, fathers and sons, mothers and daughters, all dressed in a white which captures the heart with its softness and purity, a white that has no haughtiness, a white of innocence, a white purified of all vanities, a white which has indescribable meaning.

The horizon was now blue and purple, and the coming darkness could be felt. The streets were filled with Jews, all in white, going to cleanse their souls with tears and prayers on the holy day, which purifies and absolves he who seeks to return to his God. The silence was one that I had never encountered, a silence that reverberated in my ears from its singular and trembling power. The shul was filled to capacity, the men wearing kittels and *talleisim*. Near the pulpit stood the Rav, his figure wrapped up entirely, only blurred lines outlining his image visible under the swaying *tallis*. To his right and left stood what appeared to be other Rabbanim, their profiles seen between each movement of bowing down and coming up again, each movement intending to unite thought with higher intention.

In the utter silence that reigned, the melody that is comparable to none rose and pierced the air: *Kol Nidrei* — "In the congregation Above and in the one below..." The melody and the words tear the chords of my heart, a quiet melody, quiet and penetrating, that takes over the recesses of the soul. Notes that hover in the air like the singing of angels, sowing great longing to rise to God.

All vanities disappear, all imaginings and desires as if they never were. Like a baby held by his mother, for whom her closeness is a cure for all maladies, so too am I attached to those sounds which make my soul tremble and ask for — for what? Only to be close to God.

I close my eyes tightly and let my tears wash and cleanse the old memories, memories of another hall where the same thing is taking place. The same words are being sung in an opera duet by two black singers who attempt, in baritone and soprano voices, to touch the souls of Jews. I don't want to touch those other worlds where I had once lived. My being focuses on this present moment, that I will never forget: a Jewish *Kol Nidrei* with Jewish sounds. Only they can open locked doors, free a heart laid bare that throbs and seeks the purpose and essence of life.

All that same night I lay awake. *Kol Nidrei at the Temple*. A torrent of anger floods me: How could they take gold and turn it into rusty iron? Why did they let me believe that this was authentic Judaism? The *Kol Nidrei* concerts again come to mind: mostly non-Jews, dressed in choir robes. They stand on the stage with musical instruments and a sound system. The words of *Kol Nidrei* are distorted as soon as they came out of their mouths, and how distorted are the heavy sounds that fill the air with the atmosphere of a concert hall.

It all came flooding back to me. Discussions about the quality of the singing as the service was over, the tumult of chatter about this and that, to say nothing of the open bar that was ironically called *seudah mafseket*, not before *Kol Nidrei* but after!

The next morning's prayers stunned me no less. Oh, had I only known that a short distance away prayer services like *this* were taking place, true Jewish prayers so different from those at the Temple, I would not have wasted all those years... But why didn't I know? Why didn't anybody tell me?

At the Temple there had been three morning services, one after the other, but the prayers were short, taking no more than two-and- a-half hours. Here, the sun was nearing the west, and the morning *Shacharis* service had not yet finished.

And the prayers were so different! Here there was no mumbling or dramatic readings, and not even a choir. It was, rather, spiritual labor, labor that involved concentration and unity with the inner content and meaning of the words. Labor that involved tireless attempts to shake up the heart, blocked as it was by routine. To return. To return to the pure starting point free from sin. The starting point that has nothing other than attachment and closeness to a higher world. The prayers and the quiet melodies that are pleading *and* humbling, the Thirteen Attributes of Mercy with their awe-inspiring tones.

Hot tears flow, as all these fill my heart and images from the past arise. My God, forgive me!

When I stood for the *Ne'ilah* service at the end of the day, weakened from the fast and the efforts of prayer, I realized just how much a soul could tremble from fear.

The *chazan* began the hymn, "Open for us a gate as another is being locked." The torrent of words and their melody threatened to overpower me. I felt a weakness of body and of soul. I held firmly on to the chair, refusing to fall or to faint. I felt that my previous being had melted from the heat of the prayers, melted and was no more, and from within the helplessness rose up a new entity, pure and clean. A new and different being. Jewish. Yes, Jewish.

A stranger wouldn't understand it.

As I listened to the words of the *Havdalah* blessing, I added my own intention: the final differentiation within *me* between darkness and light, and between Israel and the nations.

 ONLY TWICE WAS MY REFORM PAST ALLUDED to at Rachel's house. The first time it came from ten-year-old Mindy. The Friday night meal was over and Rachel handed me Ruchoma Shain's book *All for the Boss*, telling me, "I recommend this — you'll enjoy it. I'm going to help my mother put the children to sleep and then we can go out for a walk."

"Maybe I can help you, Rachel?"

"No thanks, we can manage fine."

Mindy and I were left in the living room. She was put in charge of straightening up and putting things in their place for the night. I opened the book and began to read.

"Amy," Mindy turned to me, her red ponytail bouncing, "would you mind if I asked you some questions?"

"Not at all," I answered.

"My mother doesn't like it when I ask people too many questions," whispered Mindy. "She says that I'm too inquisitive. Actually, it's true," she went on, with a smile that lit up her freckled face. "But sometimes I can't help it!" She continued arranging the chairs in their places around the cleared table. "This justifies my staying in the living room with you," she said mischievously. "Otherwise my mother would send me out of the living room so I wouldn't ask you questions."

I smiled. "I'm curious to hear your questions, Mindy," I told her. "Go ahead."

"Okay! Is it true that you know Reform people?" Was this tact, or was this really how Rachel had presented me?

"Yes," I answered, "you could put it like that."

"And is it true that their women put on *tefillin*?"

"Sometimes some of them do," I responded, not so happy with the direction that the conversation was taking.

Mindy laughed. "It's funny to think how they would put the head *tefillin* on!"

"What do you mean?" I asked.

"On top or underneath?"

"Underneath what?"

"Underneath their head covering!"

"Oh! But they don't cover their hair."

Mindy burst out laughing.

"What's so funny?"

"The women want to do the men's mitzvos but they don't do the women's ones!"

"But if they did cover their heads and also put on *tefillin*, wouldn't that also be funny?" I asked curiously.

"It could be that it would be funny," she nodded with a smile, "but it would be more understandable, that is, I could understand that they want to keep *all* of the mitzvos."

I was silent. Mindy had shed light on something that I had never thought of before.

"And is it true that the rabbi doesn't wear a yarmulke?" she went on.

"Yes and no," I replied. "There are those who do wear a yarmulke during prayers, and there are those who don't wear one at all."

Mindy chuckled again. "A rabbi without a yarmulke? And tell me, do the women really read the Torah to the people in shul?" Mindy continued with her marathon of questions.

"Yes," I said.

Mindy laughed again. "Amy, you're so serious," she said. "Doesn't it strike you as funny? Think of someone reading God's commandments in the Torah at shul — and then not keeping them!"

Ten-year-old Mindy's irrefutable logic confused me completely. How was it that I, who had lived with it since my childhood, hadn't felt the contradictions that were so obvious and so amusing to Mindy?

I watched Mindy as she jumped up and spread a new tablecloth on the cleared table, and, to my surprise, began setting it again.

"I'm setting it for tomorrow," she told me. "That keeps me busy here — otherwise I wouldn't have the chance to ask you more questions now."

I would have preferred that she leave the table till the next morning and stop asking her questions that were provoking my already chastised conscience, but I said nothing.

"Amy, is it true that they build sukkahs?"

This one was easy. "Yes, they do, very nice ones," I answered animatedly.

"And they're kosher?" asked the clever girl.

"Well, no," I admitted. "They build the sukkahs sometimes even inside the temple."

This time Mindy's infectious laugh caught me also. "What do they need a sukkah for if they build it inside?"

Rachel appeared at the door. She looked at the perfectly set table and looked from me to Mindy. She sighed and said, "All the signs indicate that there was a cross-examination here!"

This time both Mindy and I laughed together.

The second time my Reform connections were mentioned, it was a far more serious matter. Rachel's father asked to speak to me one Saturday night. Even though I had been a regular guest in their home on Shabbos and holidays, he had never had a long conversation with me. Of course he had always welcomed me and asked how I and my family were, and exchanged a few words with me when talking about the weekly Torah portion, or when Rachel and I were studying a specific topic together, but he had never spoken at length with me on a non-Torah topic. And because of that I was surprised.

I was shy in his presence. He apologized about touching upon a sensitive subject but, he explained, because it involved the good of the community and he thought that I might be able to assist in the matter, he had decided to appeal to me.

"Have you heard about the plans to build another shul on Lake Drive? An Orthodox shul, of course."

"No, I haven't," I replied, surprised.

"We submitted a detailed plan for a shul to the building commissioner's office in City Hall," Rachel's father continued, "and the plan was rejected outright because the Reform are adamantly opposed to it." Now I understood how the matter was connected to me! "At first they rejected us," he said, "because of problems in the plan, so we suggested we go to a well-known architect who was accepted by them and us, but for some reason he withdrew and ceased his handling of the file."

My face began to burn. My mother was a successful architect, and she had designed many buildings in our town. I just prayed that she wasn't involved in this matter.

"The second argument they brought up was that the sidewalk of Lake Drive would be filled with our people on Shabbos and that would cause a lot of crowding."

I didn't know whether to laugh or to cry.

"We are at the beginning of legal proceedings," said Rachel's father, " but it occurred to me that perhaps you could use your connections with Rabbi Shneider and clarify to him, in our name, that we are not interested at all in a legal battle, Jews against Jews. Nevertheless because their opposition is not based on regular objections, we cannot remain silent. Rabbi Shneider is the one pulling the strings. He has persuaded the

mayor, who as you know is a member of the Reform congregation, and they are working together against us."

"I understand," I said apprehensively, "but unfortunately my
ties with Rabbi Shneider have been severed, and I don't think
there could be any benefit in my speaking to him about it. But I
will try to speak to my mother — she's an architect, and maybe
she'll be able to help."

The following week, I went out shopping with my mother,
and in the car on the way I took advantage of the pleasant atmosphere to question her about the matter.

"Have you been asked to work on the plans for a new shul?"
I asked her.

"Asked by whom? The Orthodox? Of course not!" said my
mother scornfully. "They wouldn't dare ask me for that. They
asked Abe Johnson, though, and that fool agreed. When Rabbi
Shneider told me about it, I went to Abe's house and taught him
a lesson that he'll never forget."

"What did you do?" I asked in alarm.

"I simply told him that no one in City Hall would give him
any projects, and that the mayor himself would see to it that no
work be sent his way. He was shaking with fear, believe me. The
next day he returned the plans to them."

My mother had done it! I took a deep breath. "But why,
Mom?"

"Why?" she laughed bitterly. "Should we let them 'blacken'
all of Lake Drive on Shabbos?"

"Is that a reason that would stand in a legal proceeding?"

"Legal proceeding?" said Mother, sending me a piercing
look. "They're starting legal proceedings?"

"N...no," I stammered, confused by my mistake. "I mean...
just if they do."

"If they do, we have better lawyers, and we have the mayor,
who is one of us. We won't let them turn this whole town into a
shtetl. And how did you hear about this?" she asked suddenly.

"What... who..."

"Who spoke to you? How do you know about this?"

A discordant honking turned my mother's attention to the road, and saved me for the time being from her question.

21 MICHAEL NEUMAN WAS VERY TIRED AS HE drove his black Cadillac in the fast lane. He was coming from a busy day's activities, his business affairs were on an upswing, and his preoccupations had grown accordingly. But people don't usually complain about superfluous success, and he was no exception.

Even though he had lived in America for over fifty years, the influence of his youth in Europe was still discernible on his face. The study of *mussar* and the yeshiva experience had left their mark so strongly that despite settling into the business world he would not forgo the taste of daily Torah study. In his heart of hearts he hoped that his only son, "the star of the yeshiva," would continue his studies all his life. Michael would be able to support him generously for many good years, and who knew better than he how good it was to "dwell in the tents of Torah."

"Be careful!" his wife Malka cried out suddenly. The Honda in front of them quickly crossed three lanes to the left. Michael held the steering wheel and maneuvered with quick presses on the brakes; a sudden stop on this road could end in disaster.

Returning to his thoughts, he was pleased that Malka shared his hopes for their son. As a Holocaust survivor, she had wished with every fiber of her being to build a family that would remind her of the one she had lost. The Holy One, Blessed be

He, had agreed, and the single son that was born to them was becoming a true Torah scholar. "Just as my grandfather and my father and my brother did until their last breath," Malka had prayed, "so may my son do, so that the crown of Torah study not depart from our family." Their son David had fulfilled their wishes completely.

"He is one of the select of our yeshiva," the Rosh Yeshiva had told them. He loved David as a son.

"Is David coming home for Shabbos?" Michael asked his wife.

"Yes," she replied with a smile. "I see you miss him too."

Rain began to fall, and turned too quickly into a downpour. Michael concentrated on driving, which was becoming more difficult from moment to moment. It was pleasant for him to imagine the journey ending, and driving up the driveway of their beautiful home on Riverdale Boulevard. Hard, driving rain continued to come down.

In his mind's eye he imagined their roses in the rain, the droplets glistening on the velvet petals. The beautiful garden relaxed him, especially after a tiring and exhausting day at work, like today.

The Honda appeared again suddenly in the right lane. "Obviously drunk," Michael muttered in alarm. The Honda cut right in front of him and Michael's foot automatically pressed on the brakes. He gripped the steering wheel as two cars crashed forcefully into his.

The efforts of the recovery team took a long time, too much time, and only bodies were taken out of the crushed and distorted Cadillac.

*   *   *

David remembered the moment when he was called out in the middle of the study session to come to the Rosh Yeshiva's office, something very unusual. He walked towards the room, preoccupied with a Gemara question that had been bothering him for several hours. He wouldn't leave it without a solution. It was not for nothing that he had been included in the list of geniuses at his yeshiva, a list made up of those students like himself who had been graced by God with phenomenal memory and analytical ability. In addition to that was the immense toil he had invested, continued and consistent work, until he succeeded in understanding a subject fully.

He didn't try to guess why the Rosh Yeshiva was calling him out in the middle of the *seder*. As always he pushed aside any thought that wasn't connected directly to his studies. Only complete concentration brought forth worthwhile fruits from study.

When the door opened, he was suddenly seized with dread. The tormented faces of the Rosh Yeshiva and his two head Rabbinical teachers looked terrifying. He was certain that something had happened — but what could have happened that was connected to him? They waited until he sat down, and then very slowly began to speak to him.

"Your parents were in a serious car accident," said the Rosh Yeshiva. "David, they were very badly hurt."

"Where are they?" asked David in a strangled voice.

"In Central Hospital."

David hurried to the door. "I'd better go to them immediately," he mumbled.

"There's no reason to hurry, David," said the head Rabbinical teacher softly.

David gripped the back of the chair strongly, the bitter news seeping into his consciousness with those terrible words.

He dropped slowly into the chair, fumbling to hold onto something firm, while the ground shifted beneath him and his whole world collapsed and fell.

Someone came into the room wearing a doctor's white coat; was it a doctor? And what was he doing here?

A nightmare had enveloped him. Would it be gone when he

woke up? And when would he wake up?

*   *   *

He sat *shivah* with his aunt, his father's sister, the only relative that was left. His grandfather and grandmother had passed away several years before. On his mother's side there were no mourners. They had all perished in the Holocaust. In terrible loneliness he sat *shivah*, and in that same loneliness he returned to the yeshiva to study. Although he was surrounded by people who comforted him, he felt utter loneliness. He was left without the parents who had showered him with love, warmth, and hope that he would continue the family that had mostly been cut down, the heritage of Torah and of the continuing generations.

And now there remained only a solitary link in the chain.

At the yeshiva everyone did everything they could to lessen his pain.

He was a regular guest on Shabbos and holidays at the homes of the Rosh Yeshiva, the head teachers, and the Mashgiach; they tried to give him the feeling of being one of the family, and showered him with warmth.

But David wanted his parents. He wanted to wake up at night and hear his loving mother singing *Tehillim* as she did. He wanted to wake up and see his father, and speak with him heatedly about *anything*, and delve deeply together into a Talmudic subject as in the past. He refused to leave his parents' house, clinging to the last remnants of life left in every corner, trying to draw from their memories the taste of the past that would give him the strength to continue the routine of the impossible present.

The Rosh Yeshiva was adamant that he not live alone, so David brought one or two friends to the house, but was careful that they sleep only in the guest room. He didn't want them to be part of the terrors that floated to his consciousness and were always with him in his room. He didn't want them to know of his sleeplessness. They slept as guests, and he slept as an orphan.

When people tried to come close to him, he suspected that pity accompanied that closeness, and he shrank from it.

Aware of his position in the yeshiva, he didn't want to exchange what he had won with toil and talent for feelings of pity. Sometimes he wanted to scream at everyone to just leave him alone by himself; that they stop running after him out of fear that he would be left alone. He wanted to be alone with himself and his thoughts, his memories; but he knew that if he expressed that wish out loud they would think that he had already been mentally affected by what had happened. Therefore he girded himself with tolerance for all those who pitied him and for the various well-wishers.

The only one who didn't change his attitude towards him was the Rosh Yeshiva. As in days past most of their conversations revolved around actual learning and not beyond that.

It was only in the company of the Rosh Yeshiva that he felt the taste of the good days that had been lost and were no more; those days where he could concentrate all his energy and talent in actual learning. Now his days dissipated by themselves, they let him get into his studies and then from time to time left him with strange thoughts coming into his mind. He was no longer what he was.

With the end of the year of mourning, David felt clearly that he had lost his standing as a "genius"; he remained one of the yeshiva select, a *former* genius but who was one no longer.

He realized that the guilt lay with him, that he should stop thinking about other things while studying and that he should be more diligent. But the knowledge of this fact was not enough to overcome it.

Fewer students approached him, seeking clarification of some *sugyah*, and the head Rabbinical teachers sought him out less for help in preparing their classes. Study partners didn't chase after him to reserve a slot to learn with him months in advance.

David tasted the bitterness of falling from greatness, and it weighed on him more and more heavily from day to day, until the idea began to surface of leaving the battle which he was losing.

It wasn't an easy decision for him. For someone who had swum in the sea of learning all his life, it was difficult to bear the thought that from now on he would be in the company of smaller fry. But he couldn't take the feeling of failure any longer.

David asked to speak to the Rosh Yeshiva.

The Rosh Yeshiva listened silently with his head between his hands, his clear and penetrating eyes not leaving him. David cast down his eyes, unable to bear the warmth and love that looked out at him with pain, but he overcame his feelings and finished what he had to say. An oppressive silence filled the room that was broken by the Rosh Yeshiva's sigh.

"You want to leave the yeshiva?" asked the Rosh Yeshiva quietly.

David writhed. "I don't want to, but I have to."

The Rosh Yeshiva shook his head in the negative. "No, you don't have to. It's difficult for you, but even when it's difficult it is still possible, possible to study.

"And what will you do?"

"I'll go to the university and study medicine," said David, as the tips of his fingers whitened from being pressed so hard.

The Rosh Yeshiva's face paled. "For what, why?"

"Honored Rosh Yeshiva," David's voice choked, "I can't study anymore. I don't study the way I should. I can't sleep, I have no happiness or satisfaction in anything. So what is left?"

The question pierced and sank into the depths of the soul, it cried of the terrible orphanhood that disrupted the life and abilities of one of the yeshiva's choicest students, one of its sons. The Rav was silent for a long time, a very long time. Finally he said: "If you leave, will you set aside fixed times to study Torah?"

"Of course," answered David, as a flash of hope flickered in his eyes.

"At least three hours a day?" asked the Rosh Yeshiva again.

"Yes," answered David without hesitation, ready to agree to the arrangement that would give him what he wanted.

"And you'll never cancel them, no matter what?" continued the Rosh Yeshiva.

David nodded his head in full agreement.

"And if you feel that you want to come back to the yeshiva, you'll come back?"

David was surprised by the question. He hesitated a moment; he had never thought about that. He would need a lot of courage to return.

"Yes, Rosh Yeshiva, I would return if I felt that I wanted to do so."

The Rosh Yeshiva's hand shook as he pressed David's. Suddenly he lifted the palms of his hands and rested them on David's head. He blessed him with the priestly blessing. David shrank, as the fatherly touch and the memories of Friday nights in his home shook his soul to its very roots.

"Come to visit," David heard the Rosh Yeshiva's voice. David was silent, knowing that was one thing that would be difficult to do.

He accompanied the Rosh Yeshiva to a class as he had in his good days, but he knew that this was the last time. He found it difficult to meet a glance or to exchange a word; the terrible severance had already been opened in him. He walked quietly, hoping to calm the storm that was raging within. Suddenly he heard the Rosh Yeshiva muttering as if to himself... "Oy, oy, what pride can do to a person..."

It could have been just a regular statement that a Rav would say to himself while thinking thoughts of *mussar*. But David knew that it was directed to him. His whole being was shocked;

it was as if the Rosh Yeshiva had read his deepest thoughts. David had already admitted to himself that this was the root of his problem. The difficulty of coming to grips with his fall from greatness was forcing him to leave the system — and that was pride. It was naked pride, but how had the Rosh Yeshiva known his secret? His steps became slower; he found it difficult to walk near the Rosh Yeshiva who had uncovered his hidden thoughts. He trailed behind slowly, looking for a way to make the first step out, but he couldn't.

He entered the class and sat in his usual place near the *shtender*, wrapped in thought until the class finished; and during the break he went out with all the others, but, unlike the others, he did not return.

ROSE, THE SECRETARY, GREETED ME ON A stormy and rainy Thursday. "Mr. Fishbein is waiting for you in his office," she announced laconically.

Mr. Fishbein was just about to leave for court, but he took the trouble to announce to me that our office would be handling the Dr. Elizabeth Feller case and that I was to be part of the team that was to work on it.

Dr. Feller's story had been publicized in the newspapers during the past few days. The media had examined it over and over again, so that I knew at least what was under discussion.

"It's an important file; you'll be working with Michael Hoch, George Stein, Bill Kaufman and David Neuman," Mr. Fishbein told me as he locked the door to his room. Michael Hoch and George Stein, I knew; they were part of the top staff at Kreitzer and Fishbein, and they were both tough lawyers who had reaped quite a lot of praise for their legal and theatrical talents.

Bill Kaufman was a "fresh" lawyer in the office, who had come a year and a half ago. He was conceited, but efficient and diligent in his work. But David Neuman I didn't know.

I wasn't looking forward to working with what I considered such an uncongenial group of people, so I tried to find out details about the fourth person.

"Who's David Neuman?" I asked Mr. Fishbein, taking advantage of the few seconds it took him to arrange his tie.

"You don't know David Neuman?" he said in his deep voice. "He's exceptionally talented. He studied medicine before he started to study law, and his medical background will certainly help with this file. You and David will concentrate mainly on finding evidence and precedents concerning the concealment of medical information from Dr. Elizabeth Feller. You'll get specific directives after you go over the file closely. It's on your desk." He then said with a smile, as if by the way, "This case will give us a real push forward. There's nothing better for a lawyer's advance than a tragic story that's well-publicized." He pressed on the elevator button while turning his head toward me and said, "Oh, and I forgot to tell you that David Neuman is also Orthodox."

"Orthodox?" I expressed my surprise out loud.

Mr. Fishbein laughed, obviously amused by my amazement. "It would have been a shame for us to lose such talent. He's one of the 'top ten' at his law school and his marks vary between 3.92 and 3.96. Does that say anything to you?"

The elevator opened and Mr. Fishbein was swallowed inside. His last sentences were still echoing in my ears as I strode towards hall number three. On my desk was a very thick file, and I flipped through it absentmindedly.

Dr. Elizabeth Feller, a doctor in Dr. Norton's private hospital, had taken on a patient named Fred Kohl for treatment more than four years ago. His medical file contained full details about his hemophiliac illness. Dr. Feller fulfilled her obligations faithfully, and gave the patient the routine treatment for injury and bleeding. It didn't occur to her that vital medical information had been concealed from her by the director of the hospital and by several of the laboratory staff who had collaborated with him in the matter. The newspapers publicized the patient's death from a pernicious viral illness widely, because he had been a reporter for the *New York Times*.

Dr. Feller read the newspaper account of her patient's

death, growing more and more alarmed at the news of the terrible disease that he harbored and of which she had not been informed. She was apprehensive of the threat that now hung over her; she had given him routine care, handling his blood tests and examining him with no unusual precaution. Dr. Feller hastened to have blood tests herself, and her fears were justified: she carried the terrible virus that her patient had transmitted.

Why had such vital information been hidden from her? Who had cooperated with the reporter? Had the hospital director known of the illness? These were the questions that she tried to answer by conducting a far-ranging debriefing of the hospital staff. She went to Kreitzer and Fishbein, who began legal proceedings against the director of the hospital, Dr. Norton, and a number of his employees.

The fact that I had been added to the senior staff that would deal with this file testified to the clear intentions of Kreitzer and Fishbein to promote me, and I should have been happy because of that. But Mr. Fishbein's last words concerning the office's advance because of the tragic story cooled my enthusiasm somewhat.

I began to have second thoughts about the true nature of the profession that I had chosen. By then I understood that very little time or place in the offices of Kreitzer and Fishbein was devoted to decency or justice; rather, it was intrigue and interests that ruled the day. Was this what I had expected when I had devoted myself so entirely to my law studies?

David was supposed to arrive within the next hour to man partition number six, the one right next to mine. I was supposed to acquaint myself well with the material during the short space of time I had, but I found it difficult to concentrate. At the end of the hour I knew as much as I did at the beginning...

And then I saw David enter the hall.

He looked very young, tall and thin, a black yarmulke stood out on his head, and his *tzitzis* were conspicuous in their whiteness on his dark suit. He smiled and introduced himself. I still stared in surprise at him, as if he were a rare natural occurrence. What was a young man who had such an Orthodox appearance doing in such an office?

David didn't give me any more time to think about it, but came straight to the point, trying at the same time to determine what my position was on the file and on the available evidence. I evaded an answer, and asked to hear his own opinion on the matter. His speech was flowing, and with short words he clarified the problematic issues in the lawsuit. He gave me a thorough rundown on the existing evidence, itemizing in headings on a piece of paper. Afterwards he asked me where I thought we should start.

I had heard lawyers who were better and more talented than myself, but at that moment I understood Mr. Fishbein's comment better: "It would be a shame to lose talent like that." His analytical powers were amazing. Faced with that, I preferred to admit that I didn't have command over the details like he did, and hadn't had time to peruse the file thoroughly.

"Seeing as you are so proficient with the file and the section that we're called on to take care of, I have no objection to accepting your strategy."

This time he was surprised. Memories of my first days at law school came flooding back. Young lawyers, like first year students, didn't usually accept their colleagues' opinions without a fight, and certainly not in such a competitive place such as Kreitzer and Fishbein.

"I'll give you time to acquaint yourself with the material," said David as he got out of his chair. "We'll meet tomorrow at 9:30, if that's good for you."

"It is, certainly," I said.

"Our first meeting with the rest of the team will be at 12:30," said David. I thanked him for the update. He left and I stayed, facing the file, confused and bewildered.

*   *   *

I watched David, who had sat for four hours in the same position, pass his fingers over the pile of precedents opposite him
without taking even a short break. I had never seen such concentration. I was afraid to disturb him, but I continued to look at
him in wonder. I didn't know a single student who could sit like
that in the same position without getting up to stretch, to drink
something, or to exchange a word.

The pile got smaller, and I breathed a sigh of relief when David reached the last page. He lifted his eyes and felt my astonished look.

"How can you sit for four hours in the same position without
any break?"

"Nu," he waved his hand in self-deprecation, "in yeshiva I
sat for much more time and had higher concentration!"

"Really?" I looked at him to see if he was joking or meant his
words seriously.

"Really," David replied. "All my studies at the university did
not demand from me even a quarter of the effort I invested in yeshiva."

"That can't be," I mumbled. "You reached the highest
achievements at one of the top universities in the United States,
and it can't be that at yeshiva they study four times as much."

"It could be that you're right," said David, a smile playing on
his lips, "because at yeshiva they learn even five or six times as
much! And I'm telling you this on my word of honor," he added,
seeing that I was still doubtful. "People don't know what yeshiva
is, they think that the people who study there are loafers. Only
someone who comes from there can understand. To be a top
student in law is child's play compared to the level of study and
the effort required to be a genius or an outstanding student at
yeshiva."

I still found it difficult to believe him; the effort my studies had taken was still engraved in my memory, and I had achieved even less than the person who sat opposite me.

David stood up and turned towards the window. "You see," he said quietly while his back was still turned towards me, "I left there because I couldn't put my whole self into it anymore and I couldn't be as outstanding as I had once been." He turned his face slowly from the window to me. "Here I can do it with amazing ease." There was a sad smile on his face.

I felt that I had touched a very deep nerve. "Do you miss the yeshiva?" I asked.

"I think so," he said quietly, "even though I find it difficult to admit it."

Our conversation was cut short by Mike, sticking his head over the partition.

"Are there any results?" he asked in his deep voice. "What, you've finished this whole pile?" he asked, pointing to it in amazement.

"Yes," answered David, "but I wouldn't say that we're further ahead in any real sense. In most of these precedents there was a lot of weight given to evidence, and that's the very weak link in our case."

"That's true," said Mike. "What are we going to do? Mr. Kreitzer said that if there was no choice we would wait for the results of the police investigation, because they'll almost certainly get an admission out of the hospital director."

"You must know that his lawyer can always argue that it was given under duress and so on," said David.

"Mr. Kreitzer also knows that," said Mike dryly. "It would seem that he sent us a fishing rod but no bait."

We were silent.

"I have another idea," said David hesitantly. "Give me a day or two and then we'll see."

"A secret idea?" Mike demanded to know.

"Sort of," returned David with a smile.

"So be it," said Mike. "Another day or two won't change this file."

He left the room, and David turned to me. "Amy, get all the newspapers from the seventeenth of August until today."

I looked at him in surprise.

"We have to read carefully every article concerning Dr. Feller's case."

"And what will we get from that?" I asked.

"It's an idea that popped into my head because of a story I read a few years ago," replied David, still smiling. "It was a story about a Jew who lived in Switzerland during the Second World War. He supplied excellent spying services to the Allies on all of Hitler's activities and his military moves. The Germans located the spy and kidnapped him to Germany — they wanted to know what his sources of information were. He claimed that he had drawn all of his information from the news media, meaning the newspapers and radio announcements. The Germans decided to torture him to get him to tell the truth, but he asked them to allow him to prove his claims. He sat and showed them how it was possible to discover information from news items in the papers and on the radio — even secret information — by crosschecking the information and making logical conclusions. To their amazement he showed them an updated notebook that he had prepared from newspaper clippings and crosschecking, that contained all possible material on Hitler's war plans, the stationing of forces, the appointment of officers, and the like. The Germans realized that the Jew had in fact operated a well-oiled spying machine simply by using the newspapers. Hitler directed them to release him after he taught the basis of his system to military intelligence. From that developed the system of disinformation and the publicizing of false information on purpose."

"And what happened to the Jew?" I wanted to know.

"He returned to Switzerland, but after a short time he disappeared. It would seem that the Germans were sorry they'd let him go. I thought that maybe in the newspapers we might find names of people connected to the case, or other information that might help us get testimony concerning the concealing of Fred's medical information from Dr. Feller."

I went down to the archives, thinking about that smart yet unfortunate Jew. I wasn't too happy about the detective work ahead of us after a long and tiring day, but I was happy to help David. I was curious to know if any useful information would be uncovered from the "espionage system" he had adopted.

We spent many long hours sitting in the library hall; David divided the pile of newspapers into half, three months for him and three for me.

"DAVID, LOOK WHAT'S WRITTEN HERE," I called out excitedly when I reached the newspaper from the tenth of November, and again read the small yet significant news item.

Fred Kohl had kept a diary from the age of fourteen...

"We'll have to look at this diary!" David exclaimed. "It could be that we'll find something in it that we're looking for."

"How will we get it?"

"We'll make the first try now, if you're not opposed, of course."

To tell the truth I wanted to finish this very tiring day, but David's unflagging energy embarrassed me, so I was forced to agree to another try.

We traveled to Fred's house together.

An old woman with a sagging face opened the door a narrow crack. Mrs. Kohl.

"News reporters?" she asked with angry eyes.

"No, no!" David emphasized. "We're from the law office of Kreitzer and Fishbein. We're representing Dr. Elizabeth Feller."

The crack widened a little, and the look of anger was exchanged for a questioning one. "How can I help you?" she asked.

"Fred kept a diary for close to fifteen years," said David while examining her reaction. "We're interested in looking through it, with your permission. It could be that we can find something that he wrote that can be used as an exhibit or as evidence in court."

The old lady furrowed her eyebrows in suspicion and the crack in the door shrank.

"Mrs. Kohl," David tried again, "we only want to look at it in your house, with your permission of course."

She looked at him and then at me, unable to decide. Then she widened the crack and signaled that we could come in. She locked the door, and I noticed that she took the key in her hand.

"Sit down, please," she indicated the couch. We waited for a few moments and then she returned with several volumes in her hands. I looked at them with a shudder: the last thing that I wanted to see was piles of paper with words written on them! I'd had more than enough of both for one day. Again David divided the pile into half and put two volumes by my side. I took them silently and started to peruse.

Mrs. Kohl sat opposite us and her suspicious look followed our every movement. For a moment I felt embarrassed by her inquisitive eyes, as it was obvious that she had long since lost her faith in people. She sensed my embarrassment, and said in a dry, cracked voice, "Understand, the reporters don't give me any rest. They come... they take photographs... they search around and they even write things that they've made up. I'm sick of them. My son was an honest reporter, not like them. He never snooped around in other people's houses like a dog after blood."

I nodded my head in understanding.

"Because you're representing Dr. Feller and I respect her very much, I'll cooperate with you. But only on condition that the things won't be given to the press," said the old woman.

We continued to look through the diary pages. David was the one who found it, and he kept his facial expression restrained as he pointed with his hand to the lines we needed so much:

Today I had to get additional treatment for the hemophilia. I got a cut in the office and began to lose a lot of blood. Dr. Feller received me in her office. She hastened to give me the necessary treatment for the large amount of blood that I had lost. I received a portion of blood and Factor 8, and she took my pulse and bandaged the wound. When the transfusion was over, she withdrew the needle from my upper arm. I suddenly noticed that she had slightly pricked herself with the needle without noticing; I stared with terror at the tiny drops of blood that emerged on her finger.

"Why are you so upset by a few small drops of blood?" she asked me with a smile, "I just pricked myself, that's all..."

"You might get infected from me," I blurted out, forgetting to conceal my secret.

"No, I can't," she said, trying to dismiss my fears. "Hemophilia isn't an infectious disease."

My feelings of compassion and anxiety for her fate gave way to my familiar rage. She too was haughty like the other members of her profession — they thought only *they* understood, only *they* knew! Did she think I didn't know that hemophilia was not infectious? But I know what disease I harbor and that it can infect her from that one small prick, and that she doesn't know.

Please, let her get infected, said the devil in me. I was already prepared to endanger my medical future. *If you think that intelligence is only your province, then go ahead and get infected. I will keep my mouth shut.*

David indicated with an imperceptible motion of his eyes that I shouldn't express my thoughts. I understood and remained silent. He directed me to a further passage.

I met Dr. Norton, the hospital director. "Is everything all right?" he asked me. I wanted to say yes, but then I remembered Dr. Feller. *If I could have passed that needle puncture on to you, I thought to myself, I would feel better. You are liable for much more than the dedicated doctor who took care of me. I remember*

what you said to me about the contaminated blood that I had re-
ceived in Paris. I also remember your sly look when I threatened
you with a write-up in the New York Times.

I know that my brain has been twisted with hatred for doctors
ever since that blood transfusion sealed my fate, but your image,
Dr. Norton, arouses a shudder in me. I have feelings of guilt towards Dr. Feller because of you, because you told me to remain silent and you hinged your treatment for me on that.

"Everything's all right, Dr. Norton," I said with a smile. And to
myself I added: *If I were to infect you and not her... everything*
would be even more all right.

"So, the section about the first meeting with the hospital director has to be with you," whispered David. "Look for it please."

I held out the volume in my hand to him, he looked at me
for a minute and then a flicker of understanding lit up his eyes.
"You're tired?"

"I don't know if I'm tired or not but what is certain is that I'm
not focused enough to find it." Out of the corner of my eye I felt
that Mrs. Kohl was looking at me attentively.

David quickly perused the pages I had given him. "I found
it," he said.

...when the terrible knowledge about my disease was verified by the
repeat tests, I was asked to go down with my medical file to the office of Dr. Norton, the hospital director.

"Your immune system is in the last stages of collapse," he said.
Any minor illness can destroy your body slowly." Dr. Norton didn't
turn his glance towards me; he turned his face to me only after he
had finished writing all sorts of notes at his desk, adjusted his
glasses, and scratched his balding forehead.

When he deigned to look my way, he asked me formally for my
medical file.

"Where did you receive your last blood transfusion?" he asked
as he read.

"In Paris," I said.

He spat out an invective, "Is that what they do there, give blood transfusions full of viruses to hemophiliacs?"

I nodded. "I was undergoing tests there just as that whole affair was publicized in the media. I was afraid that the transfusion that I got was also contaminated, and unfortunately my fears were realized."

The doctor remained quiet. "Your situation is very serious," he said finally.

"I know," I replied dryly.

"Dr. Braun refuses to continue treating you."

I jumped from my place as if a snake had bitten me. "What do you mean?"

"Sit down, sit down please," he went on. "You must understand the danger of infection from you is very high because you need frequent transfusions. It would be enough for the doctor to get a slight prick from the needle that was used to inject you, for him to get infected. Dr. Braun is simply afraid — that's all."

"Are you telling me that I won't receive medical treatment from your hospital anymore?"

"My hospital," said the doctor, "is a private hospital." He emphasized on the word *private*. "You will not be able to continue your treatment here. You'll have to find a different hospital."

"Doctor," I burst out in rage, "to you I may be a just another patient with a disease, but I am a news reporter by profession. I will publicize in the *New York Times* the 'humanitarian words' that I've heard from you here, as well as those of Dr. Braun. After one such article, you'll be able to say good-bye to your private hospital!"

A heavy silence fell over the room.

"Sit, sit down..." the doctor told me in his authoritative voice. He again perused my medical file, as if some scribbling in Latin would be the saving solution. I continued to sit, waiting for the verdict.

Finally he spoke. "There is one way and only one way that you can continue to receive medical treatment here." He looked at me squarely in the eyes. "And that is if you and I keep the fact of your disease a secret."

"And Dr. Braun?" I commented cynically.

"I'll make sure he leaves," he replied quietly. "He will become interested in medical research at a considerable distance from here. I'll put you in the hands of a specialist, and they are usually very careful. And let's hope that a chance prick of a needle or something similar won't happen. You'll have to keep absolutely quiet and I'll carry out the necessary changes in your medical file." He looked at me again. "Does that sound all right to you?" His voice was smooth as velvet.

I abhorred the hypocrisy and lying that he was proposing, but I understood very well that this was the only way I could continue to receive medical treatment in a good hospital that was close to my home and place of work. It was the only way I could prolong my life.

I nodded my head in agreement.

Dr. Norton took some papers and began to fill them out, with all the details of my childhood illnesses and the hemophilia. Not a word was mentioned about my present illness. He tore up the old file and put the pieces into the chemical waste bin.

"I'll return your file to its place, Mr. Kohl. Dr. Braun will be on his way two weeks from today." He shook my hand. I saw his sly eyes looking at me victoriously.

I left the room, exhausted and beaten. The crime that had been done to me was awful, but here I was in a position in which I could do a similar crime to others.

Two weeks later I called the hospital. "Dr. Braun, please," I said in an authoritative tone.

"Dr. Braun," replied the voice from the hospital, "has left to conduct research in another state."

"When will he be back?"

"I don't know. It may be a matter of several years."

"I understand," I said. "And who is replacing him?"

"Dr. Kleiner."

"A specialist?" I asked.

"Of course," answered the voice, this time in surprise.

"Thank you," I mumbled and returned the receiver to its place. It would seem that Dr. Norton did keep to his word, so that there was nothing I could do but keep to my word too and remain silent.

David placed his finger under the name: *Dr. Braun.*

"We'll have to locate him."

I nodded my head.

He continued to leaf through, then he stopped and pointed to the following passage:

> Dr. Kleiner is leaving the hospital. A doctor by the name of Elizabeth Feller will be treating me. Thank God, no mishap ever occurred with the transfusions. Dr. Kleiner was extremely careful during each and every treatment.
>
> Dr. Elizabeth Feller is less careful; she doesn't wear gloves. She is very kind, greets me with friendliness, and asks how I am. When my mood is gloomy she tries to encourage me: "Why are you so downcast? Hemophilia isn't a pernicious disease."
>
> As usual I tell her that the loss of blood weakens me considerably, that the treatments interfere quite a lot with my work as a news reporter.

David marked the pages with pieces of paper, closed the volumes and placed them on the table.

"Mrs. Kohl, I think that we've found what we're looking for. Will you permit us to photocopy the pages?"

"How many pages do you have to copy?" she asked.

"Five."

"Are *you* willing to wait here until he comes back?" Mrs. Kohl asked me. She was very suspicious. I was afraid that she was capable of tying me up in the chair if David didn't return quickly. I nodded my consent.

David left with two volumes, but not before he showed Mrs. Kohl the pages he was taking to photocopy.

"You know," Mrs. Kohl said, turning to me, "yesterday I visited Dr. Feller, and her condition is already quite serious. She's terribly weak, almost like Fred was before he...he died. I'm so sorry about her. She was the doctor who took the best care of Fred... he liked her too."

"She agrees to talk to you?" I asked spontaneously.

"Well, at first she didn't want to see me," sighed Mrs. Kohl. "I explained to her that Fred had threatened suicide if we revealed anything about his disease. She said, 'You should have told me, and I would have continued to treat him. I would just have been more careful.' But since then, she agrees to talk with me."

"Fred told you that she had pricked herself with his needle?"

"Yes. Why do you ask?" she replied suspiciously.

I shrugged my shoulders. "Information in this direction can help with Dr. Feller's case."

"I'd be happy to help Dr. Feller in any way I can," she said, wiping away tears from her eyes.

David returned quickly, held out the volumes to Mrs. Kohl, and suggested that she check to see that all was in order. She flipped through the pages and checked them, and then hastened to put them into her room.

"Thank you very much, Mrs. Kohl, for the hospitality that you've shown us and for the great help you have given us," said David with warmth and charm.

Mrs. Kohl obviously enjoyed his words; by all appearances she wasn't used to receiving compliments on her hospitality! We turned towards the door.

"Mrs. Kohl," David turned back like someone who has just remembered something, "would you agree to sign a statement that we were in your house and we looked through your son's diary and photocopied five pages of it?"

"For what?" asked Mrs. Kohl.

"To be able to present the diary as evidence in court. Everything has to be clear and firm. We won't be able to make efficient use of these pages if you don't give us this statement."

"Will you publicize it in the newspapers?" asked Mrs. Kohl hesitantly.

"Certainly not!" David hastened to calm her. "This is too valuable a card for us to reveal it."

David quickly scribbled the text of the statement for her to sign, while adding the diary pages as supplements to it, and Mrs. Kohl signed. I added my signature as a witness. We thanked her again wholeheartedly and left the house.

"Amy, do you understand what we've done?" asked David buoyantly.

"I don't understand too much right now," I answered wearily. "I never studied in yeshiva, and I'm not used to long hours of perusal like you are."

David understood the hint and sincerely asked my forgiveness. "I'm sorry, Amy, I didn't realize that it has been so hard for you."

He returned to the center of the city and from there went up to Maple Boulevard. This was the prettiest route to Lakeside from the city, even though it wasn't the shortest. I let my eyes relax on the beautiful greenery that mixed with the last remaining colors of the sunset. Finally, something pleasant and nice to look at instead of all those letters and papers!

"I like this route so much," said David suddenly. "Whenever I can I try to drive on Maple Boulevard for this natural beauty."

"I also always leave the other streets for this beauty."

"And the traffic jams don't bother you?" he asked.

"I don't really care, as long as I have scenery around me."

David parked the car very close to my house. I thanked him, and he again asked my forgiveness.

"It's okay," I said. "By tomorrow I'll forget my tiredness."

I didn't imagine then that he would return to his house and fill his quota of hours of Gemara study!

*   *   *

At that time my best friend Rachel got married. I was very happy for her, even though the separation was hard. She was my good friend and my loyal counselor, and her family had hosted me so warmly for more than three years. Rachel and her husband left to live in Eretz Yisrael, and despite repeated invitations from her parents I felt that it was difficult to be a guest in their home without her. I returned to the Goldberg's basement and I spent my Sabbaths there, trying hard not to get stuck again in the stumbling blocks that came up in my path.

WORKING BY DAVID'S SIDE MADE ME WISER, not just about law but also about Judaism. I could discuss any Jewish topic with him on an intellectual level. It was obvious that he was fluent in all the hidden caches of Judaism. His power of expression helped him also in this area, and his words made everything clear.

Once, when we were taking a short break in our legal work, I asked his opinion about the matter raised by Rabbi Shneider during my last meeting with him. "What's your opinion about the profession we're engaged in? You certainly are aware that sometimes as lawyers we're asked to work against justice or decency when we have to represent someone who obviously transgressed the law."

"I don't have any problem with that," he said with a smile.

"What do you mean?" His words surprised me.

"My work contract contains a condition that I'm only willing to represent people who are clearly in the right."

"And Kreitzer and Fishbein agreed to that stipulation?" I asked, amazed.

"Certainly, yes," said David. "But I wasn't accepted at Birnbaum and Miller — because of that."

"Birnbaum and Miller!"

David laughed.

"You got an offer from Birnbaum and Miller?" My surprise turned into astonishment. The offices of Birnbaum and Miller were an empire that ruled fiercely over the most talked-about cases throughout the United States. They had branches in all the large cities and their prestigious name preceded them.

Usually only well-known and famous lawyers were accepted to work at Birnbaum and Miller, after many years of practical experience — not new, young lawyers! It was because of this that I was so surprised.

"I got an invitation for an interview," David told me, "when I was almost finished with my course of studies. I also couldn't believe that they'd sent it to me, but the evidence was right there in front of me in the form of an official letter bearing the logo of Birnbaum and Miller.

"With great excitement I entered their posh offices. The procedure there is more formal than it is here, and after a long wait and internal phone calls I was allowed to enter Miller's room.

"He sat in his fancy manager's armchair, and was occupied with his own affairs as if he hadn't seen me at all. I sat quietly for close to twenty minutes. I didn't clear my throat and I didn't show any signs of impatience, even though inside I thought I would burst. Finally he raised his eyes and looked me up and down and all over quite unashamedly. Afterwards, he took off his glasses and said slowly, 'Mr. Neuman, we received recommendations about you from the senior staff at your law school. We've decided to hire you as a lawyer's assistant, so that we can assess your talents by ourselves. Are there any questions?'

"Such a long and nerve-wracking wait, and then afterwards no interview but just a laconic announcement that I'd actually been accepted! I was completely bewildered. I really don't know where I got the courage to ask the question that I did: 'Mr. Miller, I would like to represent only people who are clearly in the right...'

"He raised his eyes to me, and said, 'Is that what they meant when they said you were very talented?'

"I didn't understand if his words were an insult or praise. I couldn't fathom his intention. I waited for an explanation, but it didn't come. Mr. Miller continued to occupy himself with his papers. I don't know how long I sat there. I've never had such an experience. In the end I just got up and left. He didn't acknowledge my presence. I suppose he thought my request was a brash insult..."

We both laughed. "Every time I remember it, I laugh," he said. But at the time it was my first experience with interviews. When I received the invitation for an interview with Kreitzer and Fishbein, I was afraid that I'd get similar treatment, but Mr. Kreitzer received me courteously. He interviewed me out of obligation and then told me what kind of work I would be doing. When I could ask questions I did, but I did so nervously and anxiously. He regarded my 'strange request' with respect, however. He said, 'If you had come here a few years ago with such a request I would have refused, but today it is clear to us that even when the client is right it isn't so simple to prove the justice of his case. For my part, we have enough hard work even in this area.' And that was that. I'm here with that clause in my contract."

"You thought about that in advance?" I asked thoughtfully.

"I read a lot of legal literature even before I did my pre-med studies."

"Why did you leave medicine?"

"I participated in two autopsies and I saw that it just wasn't for me," answered David. I could feel the revulsion that he felt when he even mentioned it.

"You see, Amy, other than the Torah and its laws, there is no system that demands absolute justice. Human beings shouldn't delude themselves into thinking that they can achieve justice and discover the truth in every case. Man is a limited creature, and because of that he focuses on the law. The law is either kept or it is broken, and if there are doubts or loopholes then he takes advantage of them; the main objective is just not to get punished. The battle between the prosecution and the defense is whether the client broke the law or not, not whether he is *right* or not. That's the truth."

"You're right," I said. "It would seem that I was even more naïve than what my family's Rabbi claimed, in a conversation I had with him. I chose this profession from an ideology of justice. But now I'm discovering, from practical work, that in not a few cases we use actual deceit in order to justify the offender's behavior. It's a very deep disappointment for me, because law is a profession that I almost worshiped."

"That's man, a human being with limitations." David summarized the matter like one who wished to bring that subject to a close. "Uh, this Rabbi you mentioned," he said.

"Yes." I nodded my head.

'Do you mean Rabbi or Rav?" he asked hopefully.

"I meant Rabbi, actually," I replied in a low voice, guessing what his next question would be.

"Then you're not Orthodox?" he asked quietly.

"*I* am, yes," I answered laughingly, "but my family is Reform."

A dark cloud seemed to passed over his face. "In your conversations with me I was certain that you were Orthodox," he said.

"That's true," I said again. "It's just that my *family* is Reform."

He nodded his head. I didn't have to make much effort to understand that the matter bothered him. Because the subject had come up specifically, I decided to take advantage of the opportunity to ask some questions.

"Can you tell me why it is that the Orthodox separate themselves from the Reform to the point where it seems that they are almost two peoples? Don't you think that if you came and talked with Reform Jews, they would show more interest in authentic

Judaism? It seems to me that you are prepared to get along with secular Jews and talk to them, but not to Reform!"

"That's true," said David, "and I'll tell you why. It's because forgery is worse than stealing. Secular Jews know that they have dropped out of Jewish life; they either 'respect it but don't keep it' or 'don't respect it and don't keep it.' But the Reform Jews claim that they represent Judaism, while at the same time they distort and pervert the Torah in the most appalling ways. They trample it while they claim to honor it. That's much worse than turning their backs on Torah or ignoring its existence."

The image he painted hurt me, the more so because it was true. A picture from my childhood suddenly came up in my mind's eye: Family Day at the Temple...

"I can remember," I told him, "one of the big halls in the Temple, filling up with crowds of families, parents and children. It was a hot summer day and we all sat down on the floor. They took *sifrei Torah* out of the Ark and placed them on the *knees* of those who had organized the event! They began to unroll the sheets of parchment from leg to leg, from one end of the hall till the other, until all our legs were covered with parchment. We were asked to touch the parchment, to feel it, to touch the letters, the grooved lines, to turn the parchment over, to look at the sheets carefully and to look at how it was sewn. And then, with the *sefer Torah* still on our legs, as we sat on the floor, we received a detailed explanation as to how a Torah scroll is prepared and written. They didn't know," I continued, "that a Torah scroll is so sacred that..."

David flinched and broke into my sentence. "...that we don't even touch it with our bare hands — let alone *legs!*"

I was silent. I thought of how the men in synagogue wrap their hand in their tallis when they kiss the Torah, out of great respect for its sanctity. I'd never thought about it before, but yes, the Reform perverted Judaism while claiming to represent it.

*   *   *

David seemed preoccupied over the next few days. "What's wrong?" I asked him finally. "Has something happened?" I tried to find out the reason for his low mood.

"It happened a while ago," he said with dark humor. But I pushed him until he admitted in a quiet voice that for some reason my Reform past bothered him. I breathed deeply. Why was he bothered by my past? Did he have a personal interest in me? Or was it because as an Orthodox Jew my "criminal" past bothered him? I ruled out the second possibility immediately, but I was afraid to assume the first; I didn't want to nurse a false hope on the basis of one sentence that I may have misunderstood.

"Is there something I can do to improve your mood?" I asked lightly.

"I think so," replied David. "...if you commit yourself to Jewish studies."

Why was it so important to him that I study Judaism? The question burned at the tip of my tongue, but I simply said, "You know, for years I've been attending Rav Pell's classes."

His eyes lit up. "You have? That's wonderful!" Was his whole intention to bring those far away from Judaism closer? I asked myself.

David elegantly changed the subject, but from then on my mind had no rest.

THE MORE I WORKED WITH DAVID, THE MORE impressed I was. He was Orthodox and proud of being a Jew, and he faithfully observed the mitzvos; that was enough for him to become an object of my admiration. But more than that, he was also generous and modest. Despite his talents, he didn't try to stand out, and he allowed others to initiate and decide. His manner of thought and speech made everyone feel pleasant in his company. All in all, I couldn't have hoped to find a better young man than David — but was there any chance of that at all?

I grasped onto all the interest he showed in my Jewish studies. Several times I felt that he was testing my knowledge. It could have been embarrassing for me, but the satisfaction that spread over his face when I answered his questions knowledgeably was my compensation.

Why, why was it so important to him that I be perfectly Orthodox? Maybe, I told myself, because within him beats a warm heart that truly and sincerely wants to see every Jew know and understand his Judaism?

He also began to talk to me about his personal experiences, especially about the tragic death of his parents, and his longing for yeshiva life; this was certainly beyond what was necessary to discuss for the case we were working on! I tried again to latch onto a thread of hope.

If only he would say something explicit, I thought over and over...

*   *   *

I was engrossed in my thoughts when I looked up and saw David coming towards me, holding his hat in his hand. We greeted each other with a smile. Was he thinking what I was thinking?

He sat opposite me and said, "Amy, Mr. Kreitzer wants to send me to Paris tomorrow, to get material from the Pasteur Hospital. It's in connection with Fred's blood sample, before and after the blood transfusion that he received there."

This was a development that I hadn't expected! "Oh, that's too bad!" I blurted out.

"You don't want me to go?" asked David softly.

I shook my head wordlessly.

"Why?" he persisted.

I was silent.

"Will you let me guess?"

I nodded silently.

"I think that maybe you don't want me to go for the same reason that I don't want to go... we'll miss each other very much..."

The tension inside me began to dissolve. The moment that I had so hoped for had finally come.

"Yes!" I said, finally contributing my share to the conversation.

David looked at me for a moment as if making up his mind one more time. "If that's so, Amy, it isn't too early for me to suggest that we get married?"

"Not at all!" I answered happily. "If you'd waited till you got back from Paris, I would have turned into a bundle of nerves."

We laughed with joy and began to plan our next steps, forgetting the legal file and everything else that was happening around us.

"Amy," said David, "I'm sure that you've taken into account that our 'contract' also has a 'stipulation' for the future: and that is that you continue to be completely observant and keep all the mitzvos."

"Do you mean that I'll have to keep them in a more 'professional' manner than in the amateurish way I do now?" Then I answered my own question quickly. "I have to tell you that this is what I'm *yearning* to do — all I need is a skilled counselor!"

Neither of us could imagine in those first happy moments how many obstacles would yet be placed in the way of our life together.

*   *   *

As David would be flying to Paris the next morning, we decided to go and give my parents the news. We decided that he would wait in the car outside until I gave him the sign that he should come in.

My mother greeted me at the door, and I burst out, "Mom, I'm happy to tell you that about an hour ago I answered yes to a marriage proposal!"

My mother stared at me. "I certainly hope you don't mean that Orthodox fellow you told us about!"

"Of course I do!" I answered, laughing. "He's a very special young man, Mom, and I'm sure that you'll see how wonderful he is the minute you meet him."

"I'm not sure that I have any desire to meet him, and certainly not as my daughter's fiancé," murmured my mother bitterly. "I expected that you would bring us someone educated, intelligent, and cultured."

"David fills all the criteria," I said with the loyalty of a new fiancée.

"That's your opinion," said my mother, "because your eyes

are blinded now. But you'll learn, you'll see that all kinds of difficulties will sprout up because of the cultural differences between you, and the different education that you received. Don't
kid yourself, Amy. He'll be embarrassed by your past. You'll
have to prove yourself over and over..."

"Mom, even though I do admire David, I didn't choose him
blindly. He simply answers all my expectations. He's educated,
intelligent, sensitive yet has a strong character, and he's decisive, energetic..."

"This list," said my mother sarcastically, "is one that I've
heard before. Anyone in love says it a few times a day to anyone
who will listen. And you can't tell me that this bearded character
isn't ogling our money," she added.

"Mom!" I was deeply insulted. "He doesn't even have a
beard!"

"Don't worry," my mother "consoled" me, "right after the
wedding, he'll grow one down to his waist."

"And about the money," I added, "he owns his own luxury
apartment."

"He does, does he? Is his father a millionaire?"

"His parents were killed in an automobile accident, and he
is their sole heir," I replied.

"Ah hah!" said my mother, worked up to a furious sarcasm.
"The cat's out of the bag: They set you up with an orphan!"

"No one 'set us up,' Mom, no matchmaker. You know that I
met him at work."

It began to dawn on me that if David were to wait until my
mother agreed to meet him, he would have to sit out in the car
for two days.

"Mom," I said, trying not to show her how much pain I was
in, "I thought you would be happy for me, that you would kiss
me and wish me *mazal tov*."

My mother looked at me sadly and said, "I also imagined
what it would be like when you brought home your fiancé — but

not in my wildest dreams did I imagine that an Orthodox fiancé would ever be brought into this house!"

Despite her harsh words, my mother did come towards me. She took my hand and said, "Amy, I wish you, from the heart of a loving mother... that you sober up fast, before *he* does — and pushes you away with both hands."

"Why?" The tears flowed down my cheeks. "Why do you think that?"

"Because that's the truth, Amy. Look all over America and see if you can find any couple where one is Reform and the other Orthodox."

"But Mom, I'm also Orthodox," I protested.

"That's what *you* think. You think that observing this and that has changed your skin, when in actuality you've fallen into a trap. Every step of the way, this is forbidden, that's forbidden... understand, Amy, you won't be able to stand up to it. The way of life you know is the complete opposite, even your modes of thought will have to undergo a metamorphosis if you want to understand the ancient and withdrawn mentality of those ghetto residents..."

This was too much for me. "All right, Mom," I said with a sigh. "I ran over from work just to give you the news. I have to go back."

My mother stood glumly next to me. An opaque wall rose between us. Frustrated, I returned to the car. David was waiting for me with an encouraging smile, but I got in and didn't say a word. He started up the engine as if that was what had been arranged from the start, and began driving down Maple Boulevard towards the offices of Kreitzer and Fishbein.

"Don't take it so hard, Amy," David said gently. "Really, it was only to be expected."

"It was?" I asked, shocked.

"Yes, it's natural and understandable that your parents would express their opposition and find it difficult to digest that their daughter is going to marry someone Orthodox."

"I've been considered Orthodox by them for years already, and now all of a sudden my mother announces to me that I'm Reform!" I said bitterly.

"Try to understand them," said David.

I found it difficult to understand how they could accept a Christian daughter-in-law with open arms, but completely reject a young man from their own people. But I didn't say that to David.

"Why didn't you warn me that it would be useless to come here?" I asked suddenly.

"You were in euphoria, Amy." He looked at me, his expression showing me that he supported me despite everything. "I was afraid to shatter it for you."

"That's exactly what my mother did," I mumbled.

"You'll have to be prudent and sensitive in the coming days, Amy, and let time do its own work. Don't push the cart forcibly, or it could trample a few people on the way."

"Okay," I sighed. "I'll try, David. And you be careful to navigate your 'cart' through these traffic jams — otherwise we'll get stuck here for a long time."

ONE MORNING IN THE MIDDLE OF OCTOBER, I got up very early and decided to go to the office; it would be pleasant to work a little before the others got there. I always liked the peacefulness that accompanied the rising sun; the air felt pure, quiet, and fresh. It was the perfect time to make some order out of all the material that had accumulated on my desk.

Any of the employees at Kreitzer and Fishbein could come in for additional hours, to browse through the library or to complete some work. All of us had keys to the general offices, and people could show up at all hours to get more work done.

I drove toward the city center through silent, empty streets. The world was enveloped in the morning dew, and the light mist gave everything the look of a pastel-colored picture. A sudden chilling wind blew into the car, and I turned on the heater. I started to organize my thoughts and plan my day.

An unexpected surprise awaited me in the empty parking lot: David's car. I hurried up to our offices, and there in the entrance, no less surprised than I was, stood David. It was obvious that he had arrived just a few moments before.

"Amy! What are you doing here?"

"I decided to make some sort of order out of my mess," I answered with a smile.

He seemed preoccupied and it hurt me a bit. I was so happy at the small amount of privacy that had come our way unexpectedly, but he looked almost the opposite.

"Amy," he said after some thought, "it seems that we'll have to defer our plans for work this morning until another time."

"Why?" What was he talking about?

"Because we're not allowed to stay here by ourselves."

I stared at him, uncomprehending.

"It's a halachic matter," he explained quickly. "The purpose of it is to teach man that he can't rely on himself," he added while hurrying towards the door. "The prohibition is called *yichud*," he went on. I heard his voice, but not his words. Deeply hurt, I hurried out after him through the door. It was cold outside, and I put my coat on, wrapping myself in it and hiding my face in the hood. I couldn't look at him.

"Amy, don't be hurt," he said softly. "It's nothing personal. Let me explain this *halachah*: It's forbidden for a man and a woman who aren't married or aren't close relatives, like father and daughter, to be together in a closed place; that's the prohibition of *yichud*, in a nutshell."

Tears of anger suddenly filled my eyes, and I remained silent.

"Just think how many criminal files would never have been opened if everyone respected this prohibition," David added.

He's right, I thought to myself. How many crimes would never have been committed...

"I guess I assumed that you knew about this prohibition," David said, trying to break the silence.

"No, no, I've never come across it," I said in a shaky voice, "because I've never studied in a really orderly fashion. I'm lacking basic knowledge about some things."

"Haven't you noticed that I've been meticulous about that in all our meetings together?" he asked in a whisper.

"No, David. I didn't notice at all."

He smiled at me. "Now you know."

"Now I know," I echoed. "So what are we going to do now?"

"We'll drive around a bit, each in his car, we'll count how many parking lots there are in the area, and when we finish counting we'll come back — by then the offices will be filling up with people."

I got into my car in silence, and as I drove around aimlessly I asked myself with candor what it was that had actually hurt me. What was the difference between this prohibition and others?

Was I so angry because of David's commitment to the details of Jewish law? But that was exactly what I had sought when I made my way towards Orthodoxy. I had wanted to run away from tepid compromises, from a version of Judaism that had no strength or ability to warm the heart and kindle the soul that desires pure spiritual food. I waved at David through the rear-view mirror, trying to put a smile on my face. I took a deep breath. *Good-bye...good-bye to the remnants of my poor Jewish education that still stuck to me. Good-bye, I hope never to see you again!*

In the office we were greeted with great enthusiasm and the news: "Mr. Kreitzer has decided to give David an appearance in court."

"He's certainly worthy of it," I responded spontaneously. In actuality this was an unprecedented step in our office. A lawyer who hadn't been in the office for five years wouldn't even begin to dream of a court appearance, and even after five years only the most outstanding would get the job.

David didn't look all that excited by the great honor that had fallen to him. I saw him immersed more and more in studying the material, editing and writing, erasing and studying it again. His exceptional studiousness aroused my admiration, though not that of the other members of the staff, who several times made fun of the young fellow who was trying to "buy a few years" by exaggerated diligence.

David didn't seem bothered by the mockery; belief in his own path was an inseparable part of his strong character.

On Wednesday morning I got up early, nervousness accompanying my every movement, until my mother commented sarcastically that it seemed as if *I* were the one who was to appear in court. But that was almost true. I knew that young lawyers were easy prey, and their experienced counterparts were waiting for just such an opportunity — for despite his many talents, David didn't have experience in the tough battle arena. Inside I was no less worried about the black yarmulke that sat so visibly on his head. Symbols of Judaism could easily serve as a red flag being waved in front of a raging bull.

*   *   *

The courtroom hall was filled to capacity; this trial had received massive coverage in the media. It involved a young star reporter who had died tragically and a prestigious private hospital. Top lawyers were to represent the defense, and Kreitzer and Fishbein the plaintiff.

Among the many lawyers in the overflowing hall I met Mr. Kreitzer, the boss himself, who had come to watch David's premier appearance first-hand. My father was also there. In the few times that he had met David, he had begun to like and respect him.

The proceedings began. David rose confidently, his appearance impressive. He began to expound in flowing language, his arguments as polished and professional as an experienced trial lawyer, well-versed and fluent in the art. He spoke from deep inner conviction, knowing the accuracy of his words, integrating the evidence that he had collected through tedious hard work.

I looked at the jury, and it seemed that his appearance had impressed them. Even though they kept a frozen expression on their faces, I saw that they didn't take their eyes off David. I looked at Mr. Kreitzer, and saw he was sitting relaxed in his seat, a self-satisfied smile spread over his face.

As David was summing up his presentation, my father whispered in my ear, "He was really brilliant." I nodded my head vigorously, happy to hear my own thoughts out loud.

David concluded his words, and the defense asked for an adjournment for consultations, a sure sign that they had to redeploy after David's appearance.

I waited for David almost an hour in the entrance hall. When he came out, he had to make his way through a large crowd of friends and curiosity seekers, who shook his hand and expressed their admiration. As he came up to us, he smiled self-consciously. I had never seen him express arrogance, and now was no exception. My father shook his hand warmly and said, "David, we are very proud of you."

I found it difficult to express my feelings. As we walked towards the car, my father whispered in my ear, "I'm sorry about one thing — that your mother wasn't here today."

REPERCUSSIONS FROM DAVID'S APPEARANCE in court made their way to my mother's ears anyhow. She moderated her attitude towards him and me, and was careful not to say anything derogatory about Orthodox Jews in his presence. It also looked like my father had started to accept the fact of our upcoming marriage.

Preparations for the wedding were in full swing, and my parents became quite involved. It was clear to me that they wanted to give themselves and me the feeling that we were a normal family preparing for the ordinary wedding of their daughter.

With every passing day I became more grateful to the Master of the World for bringing David and me together. I had never been so sure that I was doing the right thing as I was when I contemplated my future as the wife of a man with such spiritual treasures and pure character traits. I couldn't have wished for myself a better husband than him, and for that I was full of gratitude.

I continued my Jewish studies with Rav Pell, despite the great pressure of the wedding preparations as well as my workload from the office. David was very happy with my learning, though, and that was enough of a reason for me to make the effort; and of course the classes were giving me a great deal, opening a window for me to the world of Judaism and the values on which I would build my future home.

*   *   *

I stood opposite the mirror looking at my reflection. I did look like a bride! The wedding gown suited me beautifully, my black hair emphasized the white loveliness of the raised lace collar. My eyes filled with tears; seeing myself as a bride touched hidden recesses in my soul; everything seemed too good to be true.

"Oh, it's so nice to be a bride!" Linda exclaimed.

"It's like being an angel," added Debbie.

"What do you mean?" I asked softly.

"The white, it's so pure, it's...it's like an angel," Debbie concluded.

I hugged her. "It's true, I also feel like that, Debbie, exactly at this moment. Being a Jewish bride is so pure, it's like being an angel."

My mother looked at us happily. She was smiling with joy, and there was no sign of displeasure on her face. She also loved the moment that excited us all.

"Tomorrow night I'm going to meet the Rav who will officiate at the wedding," I told her. "He was a close friend of David's father. And with that the preparations will be finished.'

"I'm glad," said my mother. "To tell you the truth, I'm exhausted from all the running around."

"Me too," I admitted.

*   *   *

The following evening I drove slowly in the direction of Rav Rosenberg's house. Traffic inched along, and I was afraid that I'd be late. Rabbis don't like delays, I told myself nervously, as I remembered Rabbi Shneider.

I was late by forty-five minutes, but I was surprised to discover that no one else was bothered by that. I was received by the Rav's wife, who greeted me warmly and led me to the large study. The walls were covered with books from floor to ceiling. The only furniture in the room was a long, wide mahogany table, which was also full of books. In the chair at the head of the table sat Rav Rosenberg. His kind face was framed by a white beard. As I looked at the Rav, entranced by his noble face, I felt a sense of awe, a feeling that I had never experienced before in my encounters with Rabbis.

Opposite me sat David, on his face excitement mixed with tension, like someone, I thought, climbing a ladder higher than he's ever climbed.

"HaRav," began my fiancé, "it is my pleasure to introduce you to my *kallah*, Amy. We will be honored to have you officiate at our wedding."

"May it take place in a good time and with great success," the Rav replied, giving this blessing in Hebrew.

"Amen," I hastened to reply.

He smiled, and asked me some questions about my progress in studying Judaism, and about my family. In the course of this, he asked me a question that I didn't attach any importance to:

"Was either of your parents married before?"

"Yes," I answered, wondering why he would be interested. "My mother was married for a very short time before she married my father."

The Rav's face suddenly became serious, and David turned very pale. I stared at them, frightened and confused. What possible connection could there be between my reply and their spontaneous reaction? "She was married for a very short time," I went on, trying somehow to lessen the apparent 'damage.' "Something like three months, and," I added, happily injecting a "kosher" note, "that wedding was Orthodox! My mother told me that her grandfather made a condition that he would come to her wedding only if an Orthodox Rav officiated."

The Rav's expression became even graver. He drummed his fingers on the table and exchanged a glance with David. I felt that I had walked into a minefield, that any minute I would hear a terrible explosion. But what was happening? I didn't know.

"So," said the Rav, taking a deep breath and returning his glance to me, "it is very important that you clarify with your mother how her divorce was handled and if she has a *get* — a Jewish bill of divorce."

"I don't remember hearing anything from her about a *get*... I'll ask her..."

My fiancé now looked as white as death, and his hands were trembling on the table. The Rav reached over and held David's hand firmly in his own with a fatherly gesture.

"My daughter," said the Rav, in a warm and comforting voice, "my daughter, please clarify the matter precisely by to-morrow morning. It is very important."

He got to his feet, still holding David's hand, and blessed him in Yiddish. I felt sure that his words were a blessing because of the waves of warmth that enveloped my fiancé, and the trembling of his hands. The Rav accompanied us to the door, turned his gaze to me, and said in a kind of sigh, "In every situation, a Jew must believe and know that everything is from the Creator, Blessed be His Name."

I nodded.

David and I walked out, not speaking. David leaned on his car; his face, lit by the street lamp, was gray and lusterless.

"David!" I cried. "Tell me what's the matter!"

He looked at me for a long moment and then asked in a choked voice, "You don't understand?"

"No!"

"If your mother doesn't have a *get*," said David, while avoiding my look, "then...then the story between us is finished."

"What are you talking about?" My heart began to pound.

"About the fact that Jewish law says that a woman who separates from her husband without a *get* is still considered his wife, and if afterwards she marries another man then she has transgressed the serious prohibition of marrying while still being married to the first husband. Therefore, any children from her second husband are..." he cleared his throat, finding it difficult to say the words, "all her children are basically disqualified for marriage, and it is forbidden for Jews to marry them."

His words were crushing and deadly. I struggled to understand. "And all rabbis think the same way about this matter?" I asked faintly.

David smiled sadly. "Your patterns of thought haven't changed enough if you're asking a question like that," he said.

I suddenly heard my mother's voice in my mind: *Your modes of thought will have to undergo a metamorphosis... leave him before he pushes you away with both hands...*

It was happening, it was happening, just as she said! I stared at David, terrified.

"I'm sorry," he said quietly. "It seems that I'm not strong enough to help you in these moments — I...I need help myself." He held his head with both hands. "I can't talk anymore tonight," he said in a hoarse voice. "Forgive me, Amy, but be in touch with me tomorrow morning. Forgive me."

I was lost, suffering, caught in a mysterious trap, unable to understand the terrible words and the destruction they held for me.

"David!" I called out. He turned to me, with a look of immeasurable sorrow. I did not know then that it would be the last time I would see him.

"David," I stammered, trying to grasp onto anything that would keep me from sinking, "you mean there's, there's... no halachic solution... something...?"

"Sometimes there are situations which have no halachic solution... perhaps, perhaps, by some miracle, your mother has a *get*. But if the situation is as I've understood it to be, there's no solution. No solution at all." He started the engine of his car. "I'll accompany you till the turn-off," he said quietly. "We'll talk tomorrow."

I got into my car and put the key in the ignition, letting the roar of the engine drown out the pounding of my heart. I drove up the street. David drove in his own car, apart from me. And that was how it was to remain. Forever.

*   *   *

I entered the house. My mother took one look at me and cried, "David left you!"

My father came running, frightened. They didn't need my words, they understood that something terrible had happened, but they couldn't imagine what.

"Speak, Amy, speak! Say something!" my mother begged me, but my tongue was stuck to the roof of my mouth.

After what seemed an eternity, I managed to ask my mother if she remembered whether she had been given a *get* when she divorced her first husband.

My mother's eyes opened wide. She looked at my father. "What is she saying?" she asked in shock.

She doesn't even know what a *get* is, I thought in horror.

My father came to my aid. "Sue, when you went through the divorce proceedings from Alex, did you go through any similar proceedings with an Orthodox rabbi?"

"Of course not! We found some Orthodox rabbi for the wedding just to please my grandfather, but that was the first and last time I ever had any dealings with them," she said. "But how is that connected to our Amy...at all?"

No, no! I cried to myself over and over again. I fell into my parents' arms.

"Amy, Amy..." they tried to speak with me, and I groped for words.

"David...my marriage...everything is lost...lost forever," I managed to say, sobbing.

"As if I didn't tell you this would happen!" my mother cried in fury. "Oh, I knew that Orthodox Jew would wake up one day and push you away with both hands — but why did he wait till the last minute, that barbarian!"

"Sue," I heard my father's voice, "Sue, I'm asking you not to pour salt on the wounds — this isn't the time, and we don't even know what happened."

Very slowly I succeeded in explaining to them what David had explained to me. My father's face grew paler and paler with each word that came out of my mouth, while my mother's face got redder and she was seized by a terrible rage.

"*Halachah, shmalachah!*" she cried. "He found a reason to leave her, that's all! So let's say I didn't do that, that *get*, so what? I'm prepared to get in touch with Alex and we can do a *get* immediately — for a little money he'll agree to anything.

"But Amy, if this David *really* wanted to marry you, he would cross any bridge, even a broken one."

Now my father began to speak with surprising forcefulness. "Sue, for years now you haven't listened to our daughter when she says things you don't want to hear, and that's what's happening now too. You don't understand what she's saying... apparently there is no halachic solution to this problem. There isn't! And Amy lives by the Halachah. This fact, as I understand it, has doomed the fate of our daughter and, if I understood her correctly, of our other children as well."

He raised his eyes to me in question.

I nodded my head. How monstrous the thought!

"I'm sorry, Sue," my father returned to his usual soft tone of voice. "I also didn't know about this matter before, but it would appear that our daughter's fate has been determined by our ignorance and our guilt, and you have to understand that."

I felt empty. The last thing I was capable of was a confrontation with my mother! I turned and stumbled towards my room, hoping that I could just go to sleep and awaken from the nightmare that enveloped me.

Halfway up the stairs, I heard my father explaining to my mother, "They're completely ruined, do you understand? This isn't a question of voluntary separation, or a quarrel — it's the very opposite! This is a terrible thing for both of them. There's no sense in accusing him, he is just as broken as she is. And maybe more — don't forget, he has no parents to comfort him," he added in a whisper.

When I heard that, I suddenly thought with alarm of David going back to his large and empty house. There was no one there to take him into their arms, to console him with words of sympathy, to grieve with him. He was utterly, utterly alone. I stood still, stunned... and I had thought only of my own pain and my own suffering!

My mother broke into hysterical weeping. "Sue," I heard my father say, "you have to control yourself. We are all going through a difficult experience now, but Amy is the victim." They began to climb the stairs after me. "We have to support her now more than ever. I shudder when I think that after all the preparations, her marriage to David won't take place because nobody told us..."

"You know, we went to Rabbi Levine, a Reform rabbi, for counseling during the whole period of the divorce proceedings," my mother said. "Why didn't he inform me of it?" she wept. "Why? After all, he's a rabbi and was supposed to tell us about religious matters. I would have done everything to prevent something awful from happening to her," my mother continued to wail in a dreadful voice.

Why indeed? I asked myself. Why didn't the rabbi inform her of the damage that could be caused to her children without a *get*? Surely there was no *prohibition* of arranging a *get* among the Reform!

"But any Reform rabbi would agree to marry them," I heard

my mother say.

"Sue, *they* won't agree to be married by a Reform rabbi," my father replied.

Rabbi Shneider's words came back to me: *They'll reject you. And I'll tell you also, that despite all the insolence you've shown me tonight, we will take you back with open arms, without trying to settle accounts.* Could he have known?

"It's all my fault, my fault," I heard my mother weeping from the next room. Through my own pain, I pitied her.

"No, you're not the only one who's guilty," I heard my father say. "We are all guilty. If we had only known a little more about Judaism, this would not have happened."

"Why should we have to know? There are rabbis for that!" It was easier for me to bear my mother's familiar indignation than her terrible crying. "Why didn't he tell me?"

My father sighed. "But you know, Sue...the truth is, if we ourselves had known of it, that would have been enough. We could have done something."

*   *   *

When I opened my eyes I thought for the first moment that I'd had a bad dream. But the rumpled clothes I'd slept in were witness that everything had actually happened. The fear. The shock. My late-night phone call to the Rav telling him that there had been no *get*. His kind assurances to me that he would do everything possible to clarify the situation halachically, that he would leave no stone unturned in order to help me. Now I had to wait.

I wandered aimlessly around my room. My future was in God's hands. Only the dark past and present were certain.

My fingers unconsciously dialed David's number. I didn't know what to say to him...but I dialed. He was the only one who could understand me.

He picked up the receiver.

"David... David..."

"Amy, Amy." His voice suddenly seemed conjured up from nowhere.

"David," I cried again and then broke into uncontrollable tears.

I heard him sobbing. That was the end of the conversation.

We were in the same sinking ship, each of us locked in his own cabin, hoping for rescue that might not come.

The next night I again dialed David's number. "Hello!" I called into the silent receiver, and then I heard his recorded voice on the answering machine.

"You can't do this to me!" I cried, my heart constricted in pain. "You can't leave me alone...with the answering machine. I need your support, I need *you*..." and I couldn't speak anymore. I returned the receiver to its place.

 I HEARD A LIGHT KNOCK ON THE DOOR TO my room. My father came in, his face creased with great suffering. "Amy, they're calling from the office again. What should I tell them this time?"

"That I won't be coming in for another few days," I said quickly. "I'm sick..." And wasn't that the truth? I was heartsick.

My father left the room and then returned. He sat down by my side and didn't say a word. My mother came in looking disconsolate and sat on my other side. We had nothing to say, nor was there any need.

Suddenly a burning image came to me: This is the way mourners sit when they return from a funeral.

*　　*　　*

Late one night I heard the sound of an incoming transmission on the fax machine. I stared at the white sheet of paper as it began to emerge, and the clear, decisive handwriting told me who the sender was. With a pounding heart I took the page into my hand, staring at the words as they flowed out of the machine.

Dear Amy,

When I heard your voice on my answering machine, it broke my heart. You and I are facing a bitter test, and we cannot be swept into a whirlpool of disaster. If it were possible to turn the clock back, things would look different, but it is not possible.

Your dreams and my dreams have been shattered to pieces in front of our eyes. My loneliness touched yours and a deep connection was made — and then broken. Our loneliness has returned to its previous state, and even worse. I am tormented.

But Amy, I have no doubt as to the rightness of the path before us. Despite all the sorrow and pain, I haven't had even one small thought of departing from the path of Torah and faith, God forbid.

Don't think I am cruel, Amy. And don't think that our holy Torah decreed this suffering. The Torah has taught us what the fateful consequences of such an action are, so that we can make a choice for good or for evil with the utmost consideration.

We read in the Torah: "I have put before you life and death... and you shall choose life." God Who created us knows what is truly good for us, and He bequeathed to us laws for our good.

Try to think of it this way: A doctor who warns a patient not to smoke is not guilty if the patient develops lung cancer. The patient has brought it on himself by continuing to smoke despite the doctor's warning.

Please, Amy, pay attention to these words. I am sure that you will be able to distinguish, even in this difficult hour, that the wrong done to you is not a consequence of our religion but of the actions of those who desecrate it. I am confident that your faith, even though it is a seedling of tender age, will succeed in growing strong roots that are nourished by eternal truths and not convenience.

I beg of you, in the name of all that was dear to us, to watch over yourself and your soul, and not to allow this storm to overpower you.

The day will come when you will see good pouring forth from the terrible ruin that you see now, from the harm that has been done to you. And you will be able to find a way to use your experience to help others. I don't know what that will be, but as one who holds you in high esteem, I feel confident that you will succeed in doing this with the same pursuit of truth that has guided you until now.

I have come to the conclusion that only by severing our connection, with all the sorrow and pain that it brings, will we be able to recover and rebuild our lives.

And therefore this will be my last letter to you, Amy.

I also have to learn from this. We are taught that the Holy One, Blessed be He, brings trials to us to teach us something, so that we won't have to suffer anymore. I am coming to understand that for me, this trial is the result of a previous bitter trial: the deaths of my parents, may they rest in peace. I didn't withstand the trial then, and I chose to leave yeshiva.

But I thank the Holy One, Blessed be He, that He brought the two of us together, Amy. What you have given me will accompany me forever. Despite all my suffering, and it is great, inside I know that this has been the moment of truth which has returned me to the "tents of Torah."

Tomorrow morning I will be leaving, flying to Eretz Yisrael, the Holy Land, Land of our Fathers. The plague of Reform has not taken hold there; there the rabbis don't cut down trees before the fruit has blossomed. I have decided to return to the world of the yeshiva. I will try to build my life anew. It will be difficult but I hope it will be possible.

I am parting from you in great, deep sorrow, but for your good and mine. Please understand...

I will pray fervently for you, Amy, that the Holy One, blessed is He, watch over you and comfort you, for ultimately He is the only One Who knows how.

I did not merit to enter the wedding canopy with you, but I ask of Him that He spread His canopy over you, the canopy of mercy, compassion, and peace.

And you, Amy, be strong and courageous in your faith.

David

N.B. This letter has been written to you, Amy, after every possibility has been exhausted in an attempt to find a halachic solution to our sorrowful situation. For two weeks Rav Rosenberg has worked unceasingly to that end. He left no stone unturned — he even found the witnesses to your mother's first marriage! He spent long hours in consultation with other rabbis, and examined every possible way to find permission for us to marry. To my great anguish, he did not succeed — we did not succeed — in finding the *heter* we so longed for.

I sat in my room and cried bitterly, for many hours. I drowned my grief, my pain, my wedding canopy, and my shame... in tears.

*   *   *

The following days were filled with indescribable horror. Even the mail, the mail we sent out and the mail we received...it all came with terrible thoughts...   the cancellation notices that had to be sent to all the invited guests, a receipt for the second payment to the wedding hall...

Everything was lost... everything... Where was hope?

If it hadn't been for my faith in God, my Master, I would have perished in my affliction.

EQUIPPED WITH LARGE SUNGLASSES THAT concealed my swollen, red eyes, I went out to my car. Two weeks had passed. I drove down the road that was so familiar and so beloved during the recent past. Again I entered hall number three on the fourth floor, going over to partition number seven. Partition six was of course empty, and I stared at its emptiness. *I will miss him every day — every time that I lift up my eyes, I will miss his wise look. His absence will hurt me at every turn.*

There was a pile of files on my desk, and I saw that someone had taken care to remind me that work had piled up in my absence. Two sealed envelopes were on my desk. The first contained a note from the boss, Mr. Kreitzer:

Amy,
Welcome back. I would be happy to exchange a few words with you in my room between 9:00 and 10:00.

Yours faithfully,
G. Kreitzer

The second envelope contained a copy of a court memorandum announcing that the legal hearing for Dr. Norton, the hospital director, had been rejected! The legal proceedings would continue normally. Something fluttered inside me. If the hearing had been rejected, that meant one big step towards victory. A very sad victory, I added to myself — my partner was too far away to reap the fruits of his labors.

*   *   *

I went down to Mr. Kreitzer's room and knocked lightly on the door.

"Come in, Amy, please sit down. I hope you're feeling better," he said. Contrary to his usual behavior, he addressed me directly, and it was obvious that he was trying to be kind.

"Thank God," I answered quickly, hoping he would not inquire as to the nature of the illness that had kept me away for two weeks.

"Good. Now look, Amy," he said, "I usually don't talk to my workers about private matters, but in this case I am allowing myself to do so. I hope that you won't be offended if I ask you if your and David's decision to separate is subject to change."

"It isn't," I replied, shocked by the fact that he knew this, that David had apparently told him.

"Now, I don't mean to mind your business," he went on in a surprisingly soft voice, "but I must tell you that if I were in your place I would leave an opening for...for hope."

I nodded my head, trying to choke back tears.

"I was extremely impressed by David," he went on, "and I don't think you can find better than him; but as I said, it isn't my business. I am very sorry, though, that our office is losing a rising star."

So there's the personal interest, I thought. I nodded numbly.

Mr. Kreitzer pulled a large manilla envelope out of his drawer and handed it to me. "David asked me to pass this on to you." I opened it and stared.

"What is this?" I asked, stunned.

"David said that he wanted to bear the burden of the costs of the cancellations."

The money shook in my hand. I wanted to scream, *No! no!* I wanted to throw it far away from me, but Mr. Kreitzer's remark stopped me.

"I think, Amy, that despite whatever happened between you, David remained a 'gentleman.'"

"That's true," I said. "He was and remains always a gentleman."

Mr. Kreitzer looked at me in amazement. Only now I realized that in fact he didn't know the reason for our separation; he must have assumed that it was the result of a quarrel. My last words left him confused.

"If you need anything, Amy, I will be happy to assist you," he said.

"Mr. Kreitzer," I answered in a trembling voice, giving a silent thanks for the sunglasses that hid my eyes, "I would appreciate it very much if you would spare me further conversations about this subject. I'm not yet ready for it."

"Of course," he said nodding. "I understand."

I left his room, holding the white envelope which felt like glowing coals in my hand.

*   *   *

At supper, my parents told me that a registered letter had arrived from the wedding hall management with a request to pay 30 percent of the original amount as compensation for the cancellation. I could have predicted my mother's next words: "What did he think, that he could run away to Israel and also run away from the payments?"

I opened my briefcase, removed the envelope that Mr. Kreitzer had given me, and silently placed it in front of my mother.

"What's this?" she asked in surprise.

"It's what he left with Mr. Kreitzer before he 'ran away' to Israel."

After a long silence prevailed, my mother opened the envelope, staring in surprise at the 70 bills of $100 each.

"It's too much," she said finally. Again there was silence. My father spoke. "I knew that he was a decent person from the first moment," he said quietly.

"I'm sorry," my mother said immediately. She handed me the envelope. "Amy, take this money for yourself. Your father and I will pay what has to be paid."

Again I had the envelope in my hands and it burned like fire. What would its true destination be? I didn't know yet.

*   *   *

I didn't allow myself to look at the calendar as the days went by, afraid to meet my wedding date... but despite all my attempts, the night of the wedding came... and there was none. I imagined to myself how, somewhere in Israel, David was also sitting alone, huddled up in a hidden corner of a yeshiva study-hall, thinking about what might have been but would never be.

I picked up the final letter he had faxed me, and read it again... and again...trying to connect all the threads that had connected us and were to have become such a strong bond, but that had become scattered by the wind. *The day will come when you will see good pouring forth from the terrible ruin that you see now, from the harm that has been done to you. And you will be able to find a way to use your experience to help others.*

The only germ of hope in that letter was those words, and they ran through my head over and over.

Was it really within my power to see good flourishing from the devastation?

I went out into the dark street. I walked back and forth, ignoring the chill of the cold night, the night that was to have been my wedding night, an atonement. Instead it had become a day of mourning.

I continued to walk, and I stopped at a small neighborhood park and sat on a bench. I lifted my eyes to the clear night sky, which was studded with stars. Suddenly my heart opened and tears flowed down my cheeks. "Master of the world," I cried. "Master of the world, You know that I don't understand anything, not why this has happened to me, not what the purpose of this suffering is. But I believe that You know, and that You have done it with law and justice. Please, oh please, give me the strength to overcome the pain, Master of the world, give me the strength to continue, give me hope... a future..."

I was crying out loud now, and I continued to pray from my broken heart.

"I chose the path of Torah, the path of truth, yet it has dealt me a terrible blow, just as Abraham's trials came after he followed You without asking or doubting. But You spoke to him at the hour that You asked from him that which was dearer to him than anything, at the binding of Isaac. Speak to me too! I do not hear Your voice and I don't know what to do. Show me the way that I should take! I don't want to return to the world of Rabbi Shneider, no, not ever!"

I buried my head in my hands. My strength had given out.

I sat there maybe an hour, maybe two, under the canopy of the sky and of the trees, waiting for salvation. And it came... in the form of an idea that slowly took form and breathed hope into me.

Is this an answer from You, Master of the world? I whispered.

I ENTERED MR. KREITZER'S ROOM AT THE exact time of the meeting I had requested.

"At your service, Amy," he said, raising his eyes from his desk.

"Thanks, Mr. Kreitzer. I want to ask you for a specialization in my job."

He raised his eyebrows, waiting to hear what I was talking about.

"I would like to handle the divorce agreements that come to our office."

He stared at me for a long moment. "What do you have to offer in this area?"

"My economics studies, and the two courses, that I passed with distinction, in preparing agreements, and maybe my sociology studies," I replied. I was ready for his question.

"If you had come last week with this request, Amy, I would have rejected it on the spot," he said slowly, "but it's your luck that James Rand, who handled the preparation of divorce agreements in our office, has asked me to release him from his contract in order to specialize in another field. I told him that it wasn't possible... but if you take his place, then I'll let him go — but not before he trains you properly!" Mr. Kreitzer concluded with a smile.

"So, Amy, congratulations! Office number 211 will now be all yours. You'll have three assistants and two secretaries. I'll give you a week to get organized."

I thanked him warmly.

The first step of my plan had succeeded. I approached the next step with some apprehension.

*   *   *

I was filled with mixed feelings as I approached Rav Rosenberg's house. It was in this house that disaster had descended on me, it was in this house that I had learned there was no hope of salvation from that disaster, and it was to this house that I was returning willingly.

I knocked lightly. The Rav's wife greeted me with a friendly smile and led me to the large room I remembered so well. At the head of the table sat Rav Rosenberg, engrossed in his studies. I stood in silence facing his radiant appearance. Suddenly he raised his eyes and saw me. I saw recognition in his eyes, and something else as well — pain and commiseration.

"Sit down, my daughter," he said gently, waiting.

I began to tell him of my decision. "HaRav, I work for a legal firm and I have asked to be allowed to handle divorce agreements. I have decided that I want to devote myself to making sure that others do not suffer as I have. If I explain to every divorcing Jewish couple assisted by our firm — and unfortunately there are many, as I'm sure you know — just how important it is to prepare a halachic *get*, then I think that I will succeed in preventing unnecessary pain and suffering."

"Blessed be you to Hashem, my daughter!" said the Rav. His words blazed with the warmth of his heart.

I was very moved, but I did not let the tears that suddenly filled my eyes deter me from continuing what I wanted to say.

"HaRav," I said, "in order for my idea to succeed, I need the cooperation of a Rabbinic *Beis Din* that will handle the proceedings expeditiously. Couples like these are likely to reject the process of preparing a *get* if it entails bureaucratic entanglement or

high costs. I've already taken care of the financial problem," I
went on quietly. "I have a fund of $7,000 for the purpose. As for
the *Beis Din* I am asking that the Rav take care of that."

Rav Rosenberg thought for a moment and then said, "My
daughter, I will see that another two well-known Rabbanim join
me, together with a God-fearing *sofer*, and we will be ready for
your call at any time." He thought again and then added: "At
any time — that is to say, even during the very late hours of the
night or very early in the morning. Call us at any moment that
you need us. In order to prevent marriage disqualifications from
afflicting the People of Israel, my colleagues will most certainly
agree that we must spare no effort. These are the 'capital of-
fenses' of our generation," he said in sorrow.

I smiled in relief. "That's all I wanted," I said. Then the Rav
turned to me and asked me about my personal plans for the future. I understood his delicate question, and I told him that I had
decided not to marry, and to dedicate my life to preventing others from creating tragic situations such as mine.

The Rav explained to me again what he had told me previously — that Jewish law allowed me to marry another like myself, although our children would also be disqualified, as would
their children through all the generations.

I shook my head. "HaRav, I don't want any part of... passing
on my bitter trial to my children."

"You know, my daughter," the Rav said gently, "you don't
have to take upon yourself the drastic decision not to marry if
the Halachah allows you to do so."

"HaRav," I replied, "as long as the Halachah also allows me
not to marry, I would rather pay the 'full price' in order that innocent children not have to suffer and confront this tragedy."

The Rav was silent for a long moment, and then said, "In the
prayer that the holy Ari composed on the *Akedas Yitzchak*, the
binding of Isaac on the altar, we ask from the Holy One, Blessed
be He, 'to complete Your nation with compassion, and look at

the ashes of our father Isaac which are piled on the altar, and act towards Your children with the attribute of mercy.'

"I had always wondered why we ask Hashem to look at Isaac's ashes, because in fact he *wasn't* burned and the ashes there were those of the ram! But then I understood that Isaac's ashes *were* in fact left on the altar — in his agreeing to be sacrificed, not only did his pure body go up onto the altar, but also his feelings, the feelings of a son towards his father and of a son towards his mother. The essence of his faith in Hashem also went up onto the altar, and questions that he hadn't asked and that he didn't try to ask — all these went up onto the altar and were burned in the heat of his heart when his father prepared him for the sacrifice. These ashes are left there for all eternity. For the ashes of Isaac's feelings, we ask from Hashem that he treat us with compassion.

"You also, my daughter," the Rav said to me, "you also, at the time you accepted upon yourself this difficult decision for the sake of Heaven, brought your feelings up onto the altar, and their ashes are gathered and stand there in your merit forever — even if you decide ultimately to marry and set up a home."

When I left the Rav's house I thought about his last words. It was true that I had sacrificed my deepest feelings on the altar of faith, and for me as for Abraham the angel came and said, "Do not lay your hand upon the lad." And I, like Abraham, continued to hold onto the knife, because it is difficult, very difficult, to withdraw from such a place.

THEY SAT IN FRONT OF ME, BAD-TEMPERED and hostile. They had brought with them a draft agreement that they had drawn up between themselves for dividing up the possessions that they had amassed together. With every word they tried to taunt and hurt each other, and it seemed to me that my presence only added to their inclination to do so.

Karen was a young woman of twenty-eight, and Arnold looked about thirty-five. Both had made successful careers for themselves in the field of journalism; he was a talented news photographer and she was a popular book critic for various newspapers. Despite their professional achievements, they seemed very dissatisfied with life. My lack of response to their barbs told them that their behavior was not to my liking. Finally a gloomy silence prevailed.

I explained to them that drawing up a divorce agreement was a small matter that could take a few hours, but if there was no good will between the sides, then the process could drag on for a long time and demand no small sacrifices of time, money, and aggravation. "Therefore," I said, "I recommend that you present concrete proposals to me on the basis of this draft that you've already prepared. Each of you should write down what he is absolutely not prepared to make concessions on. Then I will try to reach a compromise that will be acceptable to you both, and with that the matter will be finished."

They got the message and presented me with their summaries. As expected we would need about another five meetings to reach a compromise and have the agreement prepared and ready for their final signatures.

"And are you intending to make a *get*, a Jewish bill of divorce, in addition to the divorce agreement?" I asked "innocently."

They shrugged their shoulders, as if to say, "What for?"

"Are you aware of the significance of a *get*?" I asked.

They weren't.

"It may be that this is none of my business," I said, "but I think that it is at least worth your while to know its significance before you make a decision either way."

They agreed.

I explained to them that according to Jewish law, as long as there is no *get*, the woman is considered to still be the wife of the first husband.

Arnold recoiled. "For that reason alone it would be worthwhile to do it!" he said sarcastically.

Karen sat stiffly in her chair.

"Look," she said, "I don't consider Jewish law in *anything* I do, and neither does Arnold, so why should we consider it in this matter?"

I turned to Karen. "Because Jewish law will determine the fate of your children if you marry again," I said. "If your children, or their children, ever want to live according to Jewish law, and have a family, no action of yours, even those in contradiction to the law, can prevent them from doing so — other than divorce without a *get*."

With great patience I explained to them the meaning of the matter.

"In other words," summarized Arnold, "if I care about the children that may be born to Karen in a subsequent marriage, I should be a gentleman and give her a *get*."

I didn't particularly like his formulation. "I don't think it's a matter of a gentlemanly gesture," I said. "It is basic decency not to fetter innocent children, who didn't wrong you in any way, in iron chains. I'm sure that you wouldn't want to do that to them."

They were silent, and then I said, "Perhaps the following story, to which I was a witness, will illustrate the matter better for you." I braced myself. "A good friend of mine was going to get married two months ago..." I unfolded my story before them, from beginning to end, with no identifying details. They listened with great interest, and groaned when they heard its tragic end.

"We'll consider it carefully," they assured me as they left.

*   *   *

While they were still in the elevator Karen turned to Arnold. "You know, I suspect that the 'good friend' was none other than herself."

"What?! Why do you think so?"

"Because I heard that a talented Orthodox lawyer left this office after he split up with her, and that they were supposed to get married about two months ago."

"No kidding! Well then, her motives for wanting us to make a *get* were pure ones," said Arnold. "Until now I thought that your future children had hired her services!" They laughed, perhaps for the first time in a long while.

"If that's the case, do you agree to make the *get*?" he asked her.

"Yes."

*   *   *

They knocked and came into my office. "We've, uh, decided to save ourselves another trip, and came to make the *get*," Arnold told me.

Their ignorance was painful. It reminded me of my own, not

so long ago.

"I'm not qualified to draw up a *get* for you," I said, "but I'll immediately put you in touch with a Rabbi, who lives very close by, and you'll be able to do it quickly with him."

"And how much will it cost?" asked Arnold suspiciously.

"Nothing," I replied. "It's included in the service that I provide." They exchanged glances. I didn't know that they had discovered my secret.

Rav Rosenberg arranged for them to have a proper *get*.

*   *   *

Dave and Rose presented themselves to me. "We haven't come to draw up a divorce agreement," said Dave, "because we've already done that with another firm."

"If that's the case, then what can I help you with?"

"Your mother told us that you have information that may assist us in divorce matters, even though the agreement between us is already signed. So we've come to ask you what this may be."

"*My mother* told you?" I was astounded.

"Yes," said Rose. "She actually solved the central problem in our agreement. You see, we have a beautiful home in Las Vegas, and we've invested so much money in it that neither of us was willing to give it up. We found it psychologically difficult to sell because we couldn't bear the thought of seeing our jealous friends swoop down on our precious home. Then someone recommended your mother as a talented architect, and you know what she did? She divided the villa into two parts, almost equal in size, without seriously harming its inner charm."

"And she did it so smoothly, it's absolutely amazing!" said Dave. "She also divided the pool in a very decorative fashion by constructing a bas-relief wall with lovely water lighting."

"I see... and so..." I groped.

"And so we'll be next-door neighbors! We won't have to live

together and we won't have to give up our house."

I was amazed. This couple seemed more interested in holding on to their house than their marriage. But that didn't concern me. What I found difficult to accept was the fact that my mother had been concerned that they know about the Halachah! Could it be?

I unfolded before them the information that I had. They of course found it difficult to absorb, because they had no knowledge at all of Jewish matters. I saw, though, that they were willing to try to understand, so I put it in terms they were familiar with.

"Your house is precious to you because you've invested so much in it," I said, "and even though you are getting divorced you are interested in continuing to live in it, each one separately." They nodded their heads.

"Judaism is a very precious asset, even though right now you aren't aware of that. It could be, however, that one day your children, if not you, will recognize its value, and then, if they don't want to give up their Judaism, your children, Rose, will have to erect a wall that will divide them from the rest of the Jewish People. This painful situation may also affect you, because you won't forgive yourself for not implementing a very simple process that doesn't demand either money or effort from you in order to prevent this eternal tragedy."

"No payment and no effort?" asked Dave. "Is your boss a philanthropist, or what?"

"No," I said dryly, "but there is a philanthropic Jew who lives two streets away from here. Because of his sincere concern for the fate of children who have not yet been born he is willing to write a *get* for you."

"If there is such a person," said Dave as he got up from his seat, "then I must meet him."

Rose got up too. "And you'll be overseeing all this so it will be just as you explained?" she asked anxiously.

"Of course," I promised her faithfully. I dialed Rav Rosenberg's number and he received them immediately, together with the other members of his team.

I came home that night engrossed in thought. Could it be that the change in my mother that I had so hoped for had indeed occurred? And if not, why had she sent Dave and Rose to me?

At dinner that night, I casually said, "Mom, Dave and Rose Jacobson came to my office today."

She straightened her glasses and directed her gaze at me. "Don't think I'm getting religious, Amy — have no illusions. But," she sighed, "I decided to inform them of the matter that so affected your life, even though *I* see no sense to it. I would have done anything to prevent your suffering, do you understand? It simply isn't decent to withhold vital information like this from people when you are aware of the possible consequences."

"That was very nice of you," I said softly.

"Nice or not, I would have preferred that in my case there had been just *one* decent and caring person who could have removed the fetters that chain my daughter forever." She turned away from me, and I think her eyes were filled with tears.

If there had been even one decent and caring person near my mother at that fateful hour, I thought bitterly. Oh, if there had only been, how different would my life be now! *And since there wasn't,* said a small, Divine voice inside me, *since there wasn't — you be one for your fellow Jews!*

A PINK ENVELOPE WITH TWO GOLD STRIPES heralded the news that Karen and Larry had a newborn baby girl. Less than a year had passed since they had married after Karen's divorce from Arnold.

Thank you, O Creator! I murmured. Thank You that You helped me to insist on the importance of the *get* right away. And thank You also that You let me know the results!

The envelope was an additional reminder for me not to ignore the matter of time when dealing with a *get*, and that today is always preferable to tomorrow.

With added vigor I would immerse myself in my persuasion efforts. I noted in my diary the date of the party for... I looked at the invitation for the name of the new baby... Judith. *Yehudis*, in Hebrew — which means Jewess — such an appropriate name.

*   *   *

I stood on the threshold of the plush hall, and the twinkling of many lights shone like golden stars on the heavy dark curtains. In the circle of light stood Karen holding her daughter. I could feel my heart beating as I approached them. Was there anyone who could understand what was going through my mind at that moment?

Karen saw me and hurried over. She looked happy, and soft

lines marked her face, lines acquired by parenthood, even if that parenthood was but a few weeks old. Without my saying a word, she placed her child in my arms.

"You've done a lot for her," she said, her eyes glistening with tears.

Waves of maternal love engulfed me, feelings that I had dreamt about so much, feelings that I would never be able to articulate. The secrets of motherhood were hidden and far from me, forever relinquished. My two hands would never hold the fruit of my womb.

I looked at little Judith's doll-like face; she had opened her eyes, perhaps because of the loud pounding of my heart. She viewed me with curiosity and innocence, as if asking my identity. Her eyes closed again and she smiled in her sleep. Her eyelashes trembled on her pink cheeks, and her breathing was quiet and rhythmic.

"I doubt if you will be able to understand me, precious one," I whispered, clutching her to my heart. "I am happy knowing that you will not have to suffer like me. You won't be forced to encounter waves of motherly love when you hold other people's babies. You, with the help of God, will be able to hold your own Jewish babies. You will never sit alone 'outside of the camp.'" Silent tears flowed from my eyes and dropped quietly on Judith's tiny dress.

I took her delicate hand and whispered, "I didn't give birth to you, but still — you are my daughter! And I promise you that I will devote my whole life to ensuring that you will not be my only daughter! You will yet have many brothers and sisters."

Although this book is a work of fiction, it is based upon a true story.

Glossary

The following glossary provides a partial explanation of some of the Hebrew and Yiddish (Y.) words and phrases used in this book. The spellings and explanations reflect the way the specific word is used herein. Often, there are alternate spellings and meanings for the words.

ALIYAH: lit., "ascent"; immigration to the Land of Israel.

BA'AL TESHUVAH: a formerly non-observant Jew who returns to Jewish practice and tradition.

BEIS DIN: a Rabbinical court of law.

CHAZAN: a cantor; one who leads the prayer service in the synagogue.

DERECH ERETZ: descent, considerate behavior.

DIVREI TORAH: words of Torah; a talk or sermon on a Torah topic.

EREV YOM KIPPUR: the day preceding Yom Kippur.

GET: a Jewish bill of divorce.

GUT SHABBOS: (Y.) "Have a good Shabbos."

HALACHAH: Jewish law.

HAVDALAH: the blessings recited at the conclusion of Sabbaths and Festivals, separating the holy day from the other days of the week.

HETER: Halachic permission.

KALLAH: a bride.

KASHRUS: the Jewish dietary laws.

KIPPAH: a yarmulke.

KOHEN: a descendant of Aharon the High Priest, and a member of the priestly tribe.

KOVA TEMBEL: an Israeli hat with a brim worn on hikes.

LECHA DODI: "Come, my beloved," the opening words of a beautiful song welcoming the Sabbath and recited during the Friday night prayer service.

MAZAL TOV: "Congratulations!"

MINYAN: a quorum of ten Jewish males, the minimum required for congregational prayer.

MISHNAH: the Oral Law.

NE'ILAH: the closing prayer service on Yom Kippur.

PEYOS: sidelocks.

SEFER TORAH: a Torah scroll.

SEUDAH MAFSEKET: the last meal eaten before a fast.

SHECHITAH: Jewish ritual slaughter.

SHIVAH: lit., "seven"; the seven days of mourning.

SHTENDER: (Y.) a lectern.

SOFER: a scribe.

TALLIS: a prayer shawl worn by Jewish men.

TEFILLIN: phylacteries.

TEHILLIM: [the Book of] Psalms.

TZITZIS: fringes knotted in a special way and affixed to four-cornered garments, worn by Jewish men and boys.

YESHIVA BOCHUR: a Yeshiva student.

YICHUD: seclusion.

ZEMIROS: Sabbath hymns sung at the table during the Sabbath meals.